ST(P) MATHEMATICS 2A
Teacher's Notes and Answers

ST(P) MATHEMATICS 2A

Teacher's Notes and Answers

L. Bostock, B.Sc.

S. Chandler, B.Sc.

A. Shepherd, B.Sc.

E. Smith, M.Sc.

Stanley Thornes (Publishers) Ltd

First published in 1985 by
Second edition published 1991 by:
Stanley Thornes (Publishers) Ltd
Ellenborough House
Wellington Street
CHELTENHAM GL50 1YW

97 98 99 00 / 20 19 18 17 16 15 14 13 12 11 10

British Library Cataloguing in Publication Data
ST(P) mathematics 2A. 2nd ed.
    Teacher's notes and answers
    1. Mathematics
    I. Bostock, L.
    510

ISBN 0–7487–0543–0

Typeset by Cotswold Typesetting Ltd, Gloucester
Printed and bound in Great Britain by Ashford Colour Press, Gosport

INTRODUCTION

Book 2A is the second of the A books in the ST(P) graded series in mathematics. The A series attempts to satisfy the needs of pupils progressing through the National Curriculum and aims to prepare them to achieve about Level 7/8 at Key Stage 3 and the highest level at GCSE. A number of topics have been introduced as a result of the National Curriculum. Originally featured in the Supplementary Booklet, they have now been incorporated into this new edition and the chapter on simple interest has been removed.

The book builds on the work covered in Book 1A and in many cases revises that work, completing coverage of the attainment targets at Level 5, most of Level 6 and about half of Level 7. Some of the work in Book 2A goes beyond Level 7 and this offers flexibility in the use of the book. For example, the introduction to trigonometry is included for those teachers who prefer to start the topic at this stage and to develop it over a three or four year span and for those pupils who are progressing quickly through the National Curriculum. The trigonometry can be omitted, however, as it is fully covered in Book 3A.

The text is brief and aims to supply explanation for those pupils who wish to remind themselves of the reasons for what they are doing but in most cases it does not supply a complete introduction to a new topic, thereby allowing teachers to use their own ideas.

There are some topics that can be done later or omitted completely. Detailed suggestions on this are given in the teacher's notes.

Much of the work in the book involves coordinates for which 5 mm squared paper is best, though graph paper is needed for Chapter 22 and 24.

There is a plentiful supply of carefully graded exercises. Questions that are underlined, e.g. **12**, are extra, but not harder, questions for extra practice or later revision. Questions that are double underlined, e.g. **12**, are for those pupils who manage the straightforward questions easily and require more stretching. Most chapters end with mixed exercises. These can be used as and when the teacher thinks fit.

A lot of the difficulty that children have with mathematics comes from not understanding the words that we use. Whenever a new word or phrase comes up it needs a lot of discussion to clarify its meaning and a reminder each time it reappears.

Most children also need constant reminders of the ordinary processes of arithmetic. For example, each time multiplication of fractions is involved they should be reminded of how to do it.

As is the case with Book 1A, these notes are intended only as suggestions. Experienced teachers will have their own ideas on approach and order of content. They will also know their children well enough to know what they can and cannot tackle.

NOTES AND ANSWERS

CHAPTER 1   Working with Numbers

EXERCISE 1a
(p. 1)
Revises the work on positive indices in Book 1A. Give a reminder of the meaning of the word index and point out that indices is the plural of index.

1. 9	**4.** 125	**7.** 128	**10.** 10 000
2. 4	**5.** 1000	**8.** 10	**11.** 1 000 000
3. 100	**6.** 81	**9.** 64	**12.** 27

13. 7200	**18.** 537 000
14. 893	**19.** 46.3
15. 65 000	**20.** 503.2
16. 3820	**21.** 709
17. 27.5	**22.** 69.78

EXERCISE 1b
(p. 2)
Much class discussion is necessary using different examples and including cases which do not simplify, such as $2^3 \times 3^2$.

1. 3^7	**4.** 2^{11}	**7.** 12^9	**9.** 4^{16}
2. 7^8	**5.** b^5	**8.** p^{14}	**10.** r^8
3. 9^{10}	**6.** 5^8		

EXERCISE 1c
(p. 3)
Discuss examples which do not simplify, e.g. $3^2 \div 2^3$, as well as those that do.

1. 4^2	**4.** 10^5	**7.** 6^5	**9.** 9^1
2. 7^6	**5.** q^4	**8.** b^2	**10.** p^1
3. 5^1	**6.** 15^4		

11. 6^{11}	**14.** a^{12}	**17.** 4^1	**19.** 3^8
12. 3^3	**15.** c^3	**18.** a^1	**20.** b^9
13. 2^1	**16.** 2^9		

EXERCISE 1d
(p. 4)
The meaning of "reciprocal" needs to be made clear with examples such as "$\frac{1}{2}$ is the reciprocal of 2", "4 is the reciprocal of $\frac{1}{4}$", "what is the reciprocal of 3?" etc.

Considerable discussion is needed also to get over the idea that a negative sign in front of the index is shorthand for "the reciprocal of" and does not mean that a *negative number* is involved. If it is thought necessary, the pupils could be told that $a^0 = 1$ is true only if $a \neq 0$.

1. $\frac{1}{4}$	**6.** $\frac{1}{16}$	**11.** $\frac{1}{64}$	**16.** $\frac{1}{125}$
2. $\frac{1}{27}$	**7.** $\frac{1}{81}$	**12.** $\frac{1}{36}$	**17.** $\frac{1}{100}$
3. $\frac{1}{16}$	**8.** $\frac{1}{5}$	**13.** $\frac{1}{15}$	**18.** $\frac{1}{8}$
4. $\frac{1}{3}$	**9.** $\frac{1}{9}$	**14.** $\frac{1}{6}$	**19.** $\frac{1}{10}$
5. $\frac{1}{7}$	**10.** $\frac{1}{4}$	**15.** $\frac{1}{49}$	**20.** $\frac{1}{64}$

1

21. 0.0034

22. 0.26

23. 0.062

24. 0.008 21

25. 0.000 538

26. 0.000 046 7

27. 0.3063

28. 0.028 05

29. 0.005 173

30. 3.004

31. 5^{-2}

32. 3^{-3}

33. 6^{-3}

34. 2^2

35. a^{-2}

36. 10^{-3}

37. b^{-4}

38. 4^5

39. c^1

40. 2^{a-b}

EXERCISE 1e
(p. 5)

1. 4

2. $\frac{1}{25}$

3. 64

4. $\frac{1}{3}$

5. 1

6. 125

7. 81

8. 1

9. 4

10. $\frac{1}{36}$

11. $\frac{1}{1000}$

12. 2

13. 2410

14. 0.7032

15. 497.1

16. 0.007 805

17. 59 200

18. 0.1074

19. 783.4

20. 3050

21. 5.99

22. 0.000 386 01

23. 2^7

24. 4^3

25. 3^2

26. a^7

27. a^4

28. 5^2

29. 3^0

30. 6^0

31. 4^4

32. 5^{-6}

33. 2^9

34. a^{12}

35. 3^4

36. 7^0

37. 4^5

38. a^{10}

39. 3^{-2}

40. b^0

41. 5^{-5}

42. a^0

EXERCISE 1f
(p. 7)

Children with scientific calculators should be shown how numbers in standard form are displayed. e.g. if $0.000\,000\,25 \div 100$ is calculated the display will show $2.5 - 09$. They can be asked to do simple calculations which result in numbers given in standard form and then be asked to write down the answer as an ordinary number.

1. 3780

2. 0.001 26

3. 5 300 000

4. 740 000 000 000 000

5. 0.000 13

6. 0.000 003 67

7. 30 400

8. 0.000 850 3

9. 4 250 000 000 000

10. 0.000 000 064 3

EXERCISE 1g
(p. 7)

1. 2.5×10^3

2. 6.3×10^2

3. 1.53×10^4

4. 2.6×10^5

5. 9.9×10^3

6. 3.907×10^4

7. 4.5×10^6

8. 5.3×10^8

9. 4×10^4

10. 8×10^{10}

11. 2.603×10^4

12. 5.47×10^5

13. 3.06×10^4

14. 4.06×10^6

15. 7.04×10^2

16. 2.6×10^{-2} **21.** 7.9×10^{-1} **26.** 9.07×10^{-1}
17. 4.8×10^{-3} **22.** 6.9×10^{-3} **27.** 8.05×10^{-2}
18. 5.3×10^{-2} **23.** 7.5×10^{-6} **28.** 8.808×10^{-2}
19. 1.8×10^{-5} **24.** 4×10^{-10} **29.** 7.044×10^{-4}
20. 5.2×10^{-1} **25.** 6.84×10^{-1} **30.** 7.3×10^{-11}

31. 7.93×10^{1} **36.** 6.05×10^{1} **41.** 5.3×10^{12}
32. 5.27×10^{-3} **37.** 3.005×10^{-3} **42.** 5.02×10^{-8}
33. 8.06×10^{4} **38.** 6.0005×10^{-1} **43.** $7.008\,09 \times 10^{-3}$
34. 9.906×10^{-1} **39.** 7.08×10^{6} **44.** 7.08×10^{5}
35. 7.05×10^{-2} **40.** 5.608×10^{5} **45.** 4.05×10^{1}

46. 8.892×10^{1} **51.** 8.4×10^{1} **56.** 5.09×10^{3}
47. 5.06×10^{-5} **52.** 3.51×10^{2} **57.** 2.68×10^{5}
48. 5.7×10^{-8} **53.** 9×10^{-2} **58.** 3.07×10^{1}
49. 5.03×10^{8} **54.** 7.05×10^{-3} **59.** 5.05×10^{-3}
50. 9.9×10^{7} **55.** 3.6×10^{1} **60.** 8.8×10^{-6}

EXERCISE 1h
(p. 9)

Revises the work done in Book 1A. Numbers 11 to 15 are useful for discussion with everyone but only the able children should work through these on their own.

1. 1550, 1500, 2000   **7.** 4070, 4100, 4000
2. 8740, 8700, 9000   **8.** 7510, 7500, 8000
3. 2750, 2800, 3000   **9.** 53 800, 53 800, 54 000
4. 36 840, 36 800, 37 000   **10.** 6010, 6000, 6000
5. 68 410, 68 400, 68 000   **11.** 4980, 5000, 5000
6. 5730, 5700, 6000   **12.** 8700, 8700, 9000

13. 54, 45   **16.** £2 500 000
14. 45 499, 44 500   **17.** 1950
15. 1549, 1450

EXERCISE 1i
(p. 10)

Revises the work done in Book 1A. Pupils do not always realise that a number correct to, say, two decimal places may end in zero, e.g. 2.596 = 2.60 correct to 2 d.p.

1. 2.76, 2.8, 3   **6.** 3.90, 3.9, 4
2. 7.37, 7.4, 7   **7.** 8.94, 8.9, 9
3. 16.99, 17.0, 17   **8.** 73.65, 73.6, 74
4. 23.76, 23.8, 24   **9.** 6.90, 6.9, 7
5. 9.86, 9.9, 10   **10.** 55.58, 55.6, 56

11. 5.1   **16.** 0.975
12. 0.009   **17.** 5.551
13. 7.90   **18.** 285.6
14. 34.8   **19.** 6.7
15. 0.0078   **20.** 10.00

EXERCISE 1j   This exercise is particularly important with future work in mind.
(p. 12)

1. 3	**4.** 8	**7.** 0	**9.** 0
2. 8	**5.** 7	**8.** 0	**10.** 8
3. 6	**6.** 8		

EXERCISE 1k   Particularly important with future work in mind. Numbers 41 to 50 are not
(p. 12)   intended for use with a calculator.

1. 60 000	**5.** 80 000	**9.** 700 000
2. 4000	**6.** 500	**10.** 900
3. 4 000 000	**7.** 50 000	**11.** 30
4. 600 000	**8.** 4000	**12.** 1000

13. 4700	**17.** 7000	**21.** 50 000
14. 57 000	**18.** 10 000	**22.** 54 000
15. 60 000	**19.** 73 000	**23.** 480
16. 890 000	**20.** 440	**24.** 600

25. 0.008 46	**30.** 0.007 85
26. 0.826	**31.** 7.51
27. 5.84	**32.** 370
28. 78.5	**33.** 0.990
29. 46.8	**34.** 54.0

35. 47	**40.** 5000
36. 0.006 845	**41.** 37.9
37. 600 000	**42.** 7000
38. 500	**43.** 0.0709
39. 7.82	**44.** 0.07

45. 3.3	**50.** 29
46. 1.7	**51.** 24
47. 13	**52.** 0.23
48. 13	**53.** 0.026
49. 14	**54.** 0.000 43

EXERCISE 1l   Revise multiplication and division by decimals before working through this
(p. 14)   exercise. Allow some discretion in the number of s.f. accepted for the answer.

1. 100	**11.** 600
2. 36	**12.** 4.5
3. 0.35	**13.** 2
4. 20	**14.** 0.7
5. 180 000	**15.** 17

6. 0.8	**16.** 0.003
7. 0.48	**17.** 0.0056
8. 3.6	**18.** 80
9. 1.3	**19.** 90 000
10. 3 500 000	**20.** 1.5

21. 10

22. 0.36

23. 10

24. 2

25. 32

26. 1.2

27. 15

28. 0.25

29. 0.12

30. 140

EXERCISE 1m
(p. 16)
Pupils may need reassurance that the calculator illustrated in the Pupil's Book on page 15 is only an example and that there are many different designs.

1. 7.08

2. 7.55

3. 7.02

4. 8.54

5. 9.19

6. 7.71

7. 7.49

8. 9.15

9. 1.61

10. 1.56

11. 3.80

12. 1.50

13. 2.94

14. 1.54

15. 1.44

16. 1330

17. 8370

18. 6580

19. 15.5

20. 6.65

21. 172

22. 14.7

23. 11.2

24. 1170

25. 12 600

26. 36.8

27. 1950

28. 38.0

29. 1350

30. 14 400

31. 2.70

32. 0.0196

33. 0.0549

34. 526

35. 4.65

36. 0.0481

37. 1.79

38. 0.0051 5

39. 3.97

40. 0.548

41. 0.121

42. 0.0825

43. 0.393

44. 0.103

45. 0.139

46. 124

47. 55.8

48. 91.7

49. 186

50. 957

51. 49.0

52. 11 200

53. 83.6

54. 2.28

55. 0.672

56. 9.83

57. 0.693

58. 0.742

59. 0.128

60. 10 300

61. 6340

62. 0.006 08

63. 34.8

64. 484 000

65. 0.361

66. 0.0203

67. 0.000 123

68. 631

69. 0.000 000 096 1

70. 4950

71. 0.174

72. 16.7

73. 0.000 146

74. 13.4

EXERCISE 1n
(p. 17)

1. $\frac{1}{16}$

2. $1/b^3$

3. 1

4. 3.64×10^4

5. 5.07×10^{-3}

6. 60 000

7. 0.0614

8. 3.71

9. 2.88

EXERCISE 1p
(p. 18)

1. 216

2. 2^{-2}

3. $\frac{1}{5}$

4. a^7

5. 6.5×10^8

6. 46 000

7. 21 500

8. 1350

9. 0.699

EXERCISE 1q
(p. 18)

1. 5

2. $1/a$

3. 1

4. 5.708×10^{-3}

5. 10 000

6. 0.0508

7. 9

8. 9.89

9. 4.70

CHAPTER 2   Probability

The language used to describe this topic often leads to misunderstanding: the words "experiment", "event", "outcome" etc. all have fairly precise meanings and plenty of discussion is needed to make their meanings clear. It is also important to discuss the objects used for experiments; for example not all children are familiar with an ordinary pack of playing cards, especially those from Muslim backgrounds. It is a good idea to have some packs of cards available and some dice. (We have used the plural form, dice, for one die. This is deliberate as it is the word that most people use these days, but it is a good idea to tell the children that the singular is die.)

In several questions reference is made to sets of integers or whole numbers – these do not include zero.

EXERCISE 2a Can be used for discussion.
(p. 19)
    1. 2, {H, T}
    2. 3, {R, B, Y}
    3. 10, {1, 2, 3, 4, 5, 6, 7, 8, 9, 10}
    4. 6, {R, Y, B, Brown, Black, G}
    5. 3, {chewing gum, boiled sweets, bar of chocolate}
    6. 4, {1p, 10p, 20p, 50p}
    7. 13, {A, 2, 3, 4, 5, 6, 7, 8, 9, 10, J, Q, K}
    8. 5, {a, e, i, o, u}
    9. 5, {2, 3, 5, 7, 11}
    10. 10, {2, 4, 6, 8, 10, 12, 14, 16, 18, 20}

EXERCISE 2b Discuss the phrase "at random" and include examples where objects are not
(p. 20) chosen at random: e.g. a boy taking a piece of cake from a plate—if he likes it he will try to take the largest slice. The questions in this exercise can be used for discussion (alter the conditions).

1. $\frac{1}{4}$	**4.** $\frac{1}{6}$	**7.** $\frac{1}{52}$
2. $\frac{1}{10}$	**5.** $\frac{1}{7}$	**8.** $\frac{1}{7}$
3. $\frac{1}{5}$	**6.** $\frac{1}{200}$	**9.** $\frac{1}{15}$

EXERCISE 2c Numbers 9 to 15 require an above average understanding of language. Use
(p. 22) them for discussion with everyone but allow only the above average to try them on their own.

1. 5	**6.** a) $\frac{1}{2}$ b) $\frac{1}{2}$ c) $\frac{2}{5}$ d) $\frac{3}{10}$
2. 3	**7.** a) $\frac{1}{13}$ b) $\frac{1}{2}$ c) $\frac{1}{4}$ d) $\frac{4}{13}$
3. 26	**8.** a) $\frac{2}{9}$ b) $\frac{1}{9}$ c) $\frac{1}{3}$ d) $\frac{2}{9}$
4. 2	**9.** a) $\frac{1}{2}$ b) $\frac{1}{3}$ c) $\frac{1}{3}$
5. 10	

10. $\frac{2}{15}$

11. a) $\frac{3}{5}$ b) $\frac{1}{5}$ c) $\frac{2}{5}$

12. $\frac{1}{40}$

13. a) $\frac{17}{36}$ b) $\frac{1}{2}$ c) $\frac{1}{4}$

14. $\frac{21}{26}$

15. $\frac{4}{45}$

16. a) $\frac{5}{12}$ b) $\frac{1}{3}$ c) $\frac{3}{4}$

EXERCISE 2d
(p. 24)

Can be used for discussion.

1. 0, impossible

2. 0.3, unlikely to be this heavy

3. 1, almost certain

4. 0.001, possible but unlikely

5. 0, most unlikely!

6. 0, impossible

7. 1, certain

8. 0, virtually impossible

9. 1, it must be

10. 0, almost impossible

11. Likely: you will watch TV this week, you will get maths homework this week.

Unlikely: you will be a millionaire, it will snow in Britain on mid-summer day.

EXERCISE 2e
(p. 25)

Numbers 10 to 14 can be used for discussion with everyone.

1. $\frac{3}{5}$ **4.** $\frac{5}{6}$ **7.** $\frac{24}{25}$ **9.** $\frac{39}{40}$

2. $\frac{12}{13}$ **5.** $\frac{7}{10}$ **8.** $\frac{2}{3}$ **10.** $\frac{10}{13}$

3. $\frac{21}{26}$ **6.** $\frac{5}{8}$

11. a) $\frac{1}{10}$ b) $\frac{3}{10}$ c) $\frac{2}{5}$ d) $\frac{7}{10}$

12. a) $\frac{1}{13}$ b) $\frac{1}{4}$ c) $\frac{3}{4}$ d) $\frac{11}{13}$

13. a) $\frac{15}{22}$ b) $\frac{7}{22}$ c) $\frac{1}{22}$ d) $\frac{3}{11}$

14. a) $\frac{2}{5}$ b) $\frac{19}{30}$ c) $\frac{7}{30}$ d) 0

EXERCISE 2f
(p. 27)

Can be omitted.

1.

	○	○	○	●	●
○	(○, ○)	(○, ○)	(○, ○)	(○, ●)	(○, ●)
○	(○, ○)	(○, ○)	(○, ○)	(○, ●)	(○, ●)
○	(○, ○)	(○, ○)	(○, ○)	(○, ●)	(○, ●)
●	(●, ○)	(●, ○)	(●, ○)	(●, ●)	(●, ●)
●	(●, ○)	(●, ○)	(●, ○)	(●, ●)	(●, ●)

2.

	Dice					
	1	2	3	4	5	6
H	(H, 1)	(H, 2)	(H, 3)	(H, 4)	(H, 5)	(H, 6)
T	(T, 1)	(T, 2)	(T, 3)	(T, 4)	(T, 5)	(T, 6)

10 p

3.

	1st bag			
	R	R	Y	B
R	(R, R)	(R, R)	(R, Y)	(R, B)
Y	(Y, R)	(Y, R)	(Y, Y)	(Y, B)
Y	(Y, R)	(Y, R)	(Y, Y)	(Y, B)
B	(B, R)	(B, R)	(B, Y)	(B, B)

2nd bag

4.

	1st spin		
	1	2	3
1	(1, 1)	(1, 2)	(1, 3)
2	(2, 1)	(2, 2)	(2, 3)
3	(3, 1)	(3, 2)	(3, 3)

2nd spin

5.

	Pencil		
	Red	Green	Yellow
Round	Round, Red	Round, Green	Round, Yellow
Square	Square, Red	Square, Green	Square, Yellow
Triangular	Triangular, Red	Triangular, Green	Triangular, Yellow

Rubber

EXERCISE 2g   Omit this exercise if Exercise 2f was not covered.
(p. 29)

1. a) $\frac{1}{6}$ b) $\frac{1}{9}$ c) $\frac{1}{6}$

2. a) $\frac{4}{25}$ b) $\frac{16}{25}$

3. $\frac{1}{6}$

4. a) $\frac{1}{16}$ b) $\frac{1}{8}$ c) $\frac{3}{16}$ d) $\frac{5}{8}$

5.

5 p coin

		H	T
	H	(H, H)	(H, T)
1 p coin	T	(T, H)	(T, T)

$\frac{1}{4}$

6.

First dice

		1	●	3	4	●	6
	1	(1, 1)	(1, ●)	(1, 3)	(1, 4)	(1, ●)	(1, 6)
	2	(2, 1)	(2, ●)	(2, 3)	(2, 4)	(2, ●)	(2, 6)
2nd	3	(3, 1)	(3, ●)	(3, 3)	(3, 4)	(3, ●)	(3, 6)
dice	4	(4, 1)	(4, ●)	(4, 3)	(4, 4)	(4, ●)	(4, 6)
	5	(5, 1)	(5, ●)	(5, 3)	(5, 4)	(5, ●)	(5, 6)
	6	(6, 1)	(6, ●)	(6, 3)	(6, 4)	(6, ●)	(6, 6)

a) $\frac{5}{36}$ b) $\frac{1}{18}$ c) $\frac{1}{18}$ d) $\frac{19}{36}$

7.

First bag

		10 p	10 p	10 p	50 p	50 p
	10 p	(10p, 10p)	(10p, 10p)	(10p, 10p)	(10p, 50p)	(10p, 50p)
2nd bag	50 p	(50p, 10p)	(50p, 10p)	(50p, 10p)	(50p, 50p)	(50p, 50p)

$\frac{1}{5}$

8.

First shelf

		Story	Story	Text	Text	Text
	Story	(S, S)	(S, S)	(S, T)	(S, T)	(S, T)
2nd shelf	Story	(S, S)	(S, S)	(S, T)	(S, T)	(S, T)
	Story	(S, S)	(S, S)	(S, T)	(S, T)	(S, T)
	Text	(T, S)	(T, S)	(T, T)	(T, T)	(T, T)

a) $\frac{3}{10}$ b) $\frac{3}{20}$

9. a) $\frac{1}{4}$ b) $\frac{1}{16}$ c) $\frac{3}{4}$ d) $\frac{1}{4}$

EXERCISE 2h
(p. 31)
Can be done earlier in the chapter, e.g. after Exercise 2c. At this stage it is not wise to place too much emphasis on the difference between theoretical and experimental probability.

4. $\frac{1}{4}$

5. $\frac{1}{2}$

6. $\frac{1}{4}$

8. $\frac{2}{3}$

10. 10

12. Roughly rectangular.

13. Ten throws is too few.

15. No. All the same number.

16. 50

17. About 500 heads. It is unlikely, but possible, that you will get 1000 heads or 1000 tails.

18. Any number of heads from 0 to 10.

19. Very unlikely.

CHAPTER 3   Constructions

Revision of the facts learned in Book 1A is necessary

EXERCISE 3a
(p. 36)
Revises the geometry covered in Book 1A.

1. $60°$

2. $75°$

3. $100°$

4. $130°$

5. $d = 60°$, $e = 120°$

6. $70°$

7. $p = 130°$, $q = 50°$

8. $s = 70°$, $t = 110°$

9. $l = 60°$, $m = 100°$, $n = 20°$

10. $d = 30°$, $e = 75°$, $f = 105°$

EXERCISE 3b
(p. 38)
Discuss the space needed for constructions (a lot more is needed than pupils realise). Discuss also what radius is a sensible choice (pupils tend to choose too small a radius, making accuracy difficult). Stress again the need to use a sharp pencil and point out that the compasses are much easier to use if the pencil is put into the compasses so that the pointed arm is almost vertical, rather than at an appreciable angle to the vertical. It is also worth mentioning that if an angle of $90°$ is to be constructed at the *end* of a line, the line must first be produced beyond that end.

EXERCISE 3c **11.** 90°
(p. 40) **12.** 45°
14. they are parallel

EXERCISE 3d Numbers 2 to 9 can be used for discussion.
(p. 41)

2. they are equal **6.** at the midpoint of AB
3. AB and CD **7.** at the midpoint of CD
4. coincident **8.** 90°
5. coincident **9.** each is 90°

Bisecting lines and dropping perpendiculars: the radius for the arcs below the line can be smaller than that used for the first arcs—with able children it is worth explaining this, but discuss the diagonals of a kite at the same time. Point out that the phrase "*dropping*" a perpendicular applies also when the point is below the line.

EXERCISE 3e Numbers 8 to 14 involve constructing circumcircles and incircles. They are
(p. 43) straightforward but lengthy and, for incircles in particular, the construction works only if the drawing is accurate. Able children can cope, but use discretion with the others. The formal construction of a circumcircle is in Book 3A and of the incircle in Book 4A.

4. The perpendicular bisector of LM passes through N.
5. The perpendicular bisector of PR does not pass through Q.
6. The perpendicular bisector of the chord AB which passes through the centre C.

EXERCISE 3f Use firm cartridge paper. If used for Christmas decorations, either colour with
(p. 45) felt tips before cutting out or use spray paint when completed, and remember to incorporate a thread with a knot at one end while the solid is being stuck together.

CHAPTER 4 Introducing Percentages

Calculators are not necessary but the weaker pupils may benefit from using them.

EXERCISE 4a Emphasise the common results, e.g. $50\% = \frac{1}{2} = 0.5$. These should be made
(p. 49) familiar and, if necessary, learned.

1. $\frac{1}{5}$ **8.** $\frac{1}{2}$ **15.** $\frac{7}{10}$ **22.** $\frac{19}{20}$

2. $\frac{9}{20}$ **9.** $\frac{13}{20}$ **16.** $\frac{3}{4}$ **23.** $\frac{3}{20}$

3. $\frac{1}{4}$ **10.** $\frac{14}{25}$ **17.** $\frac{12}{25}$ **24.** $\frac{2}{25}$

4. $\frac{18}{25}$ **11.** $\frac{37}{100}$ **18.** $\frac{69}{100}$ **25.** $\frac{41}{50}$

5. $\frac{1}{3}$ **12.** $\frac{2}{3}$ **19.** $\frac{3}{8}$ **26.** $\frac{7}{8}$

6. $\frac{1}{8}$ **13.** $\frac{5}{8}$ **20.** $\frac{4}{75}$ **27.** $\frac{1}{16}$

7. $\frac{1}{40}$ **14.** $\frac{5}{4}$ **21.** $\frac{7}{40}$ **28.** $\frac{3}{2}$

29. 0.47	**34.** 0.58	**39.** 0.92	**44.** 0.08
30. 0.12	**35.** 0.3	**40.** 0.65	**45.** 0.03
31. 0.055	**36.** 0.623	**41.** 1.2	**46.** 1.8
32. 1.45	**37.** 3.5	**42.** 2.31	**47.** 0.053
33. 0.583	**38.** 0.487	**43.** 0.857	**48.** 0.541

EXERCISE 4b
(p. 50)

1. 50%	**6.** 25%	**11.** 75%	**16.** 60%
2. 70%	**7.** 15%	**12.** 45%	**17.** 35%
3. 65%	**8.** 16%	**13.** 140%	**18.** 124%
4. $33\frac{1}{3}$%	**9.** 37.5%	**14.** $62\frac{1}{2}$%	**19.** $87\frac{1}{2}$%
5. 52.5%	**10.** $38\frac{1}{3}$%	**15.** $266\frac{2}{3}$%	**20.** 160%

21. 50%	**26.** 90%	**31.** 25%	**36.** 36%
22. 22%	**27.** 4%	**32.** 74%	**37.** 16%
23. 83%	**28.** 55%	**33.** 125%	**38.** 139%
24. 172%	**29.** 264%	**34.** 341%	**39.** 635%
25. 62.5%	**30.** 84.5%	**35.** 7.5%	**40.** 18.25%

EXERCISE 4c
(p. 51)

Questions 5 to 10 provide a very convenient way of confirming the relationships between fractions, percentages and decimals.

1. a) $\frac{3}{10}$ b) $\frac{17}{20}$ c) $\frac{17}{40}$ d) $\frac{21}{400}$
2. a) 0.44   b) 0.68   c) 1.7   d) 0.165
3. a) 40%   b) 85%   c) $12\frac{1}{2}$%   d) $113\frac{1}{3}$%
4. a) 20%   b) 62%   c) $84\frac{1}{2}$%   d) 178%

	Fraction	Percentage	Decimal
	$\frac{3}{4}$	75%	0.75
5.	$\frac{4}{5}$	80%	0.8
6.	$\frac{3}{5}$	60%	0.6
7.	$\frac{7}{10}$	70%	0.7
8.	$\frac{11}{20}$	55%	0.55
9.	$\frac{11}{25}$	44%	0.44
10.	$\frac{8}{25}$	32%	0.32

EXERCISE 4d
(p. 52)

May be used for class discussion. Numbers 9 to 14 are intended for the above average child.

1. 52%	**4.** 92%	**7.** 43%
2. 13%	**5.** 88%	**8.** 68%
3. 36%	**6.** 12%	

9. 20%	**12.** 252
10. 38%	**13.** 1400
11. 3%	**14.** a) 2% b) 10% c) 66% d) 22%

EXERCISE 4e
(p. 53)
Although nearly all the questions give numbers with units, none of the answers involve units. Discussion of "What has happened to the units" is worthwhile. In some questions it is necessary to make the units compatible.

1. 25%   **3.** $33\frac{1}{3}$%   **5.** 75%   **7.** 15%
2. 60%   **4.** $33\frac{1}{3}$%   **6.** 60%   **8.** 25%

9. 10%   **11.** 30%   **13.** 200%   **15.** 10%
10. 20%   **12.** 50%   **14.** $62\frac{1}{2}$%   **16.** $66\frac{2}{3}$%

17. 25%   **20.** 40%   **23.** 72%   **25.** 72%
18. $37\frac{1}{2}$%   **21.** 60%   **24.** $333\frac{1}{3}$%   **26.** 42%
19. 20%   **22.** 25%

27. 40%   **30.** $66\frac{2}{3}$%   **33.** $33\frac{1}{3}$%   **35.** $13\frac{1}{3}$%
28. 65%   **31.** $2\frac{1}{2}$%   **34.** 4%   **36.** $2\frac{1}{2}$%
29. $23\frac{1}{3}$%   **32.** 36%

37. 0.46%   **40.** 25%   **43.** $2\frac{1}{2}$%   **45.** $666\frac{2}{3}$%
38. 500%   **41.** 400%   **44.** 25%   **46.** 8%
39. 65%   **42.** 10%

EXERCISE 4f
(p. 55)
1. 48   **4.** 286 km   **7.** 252   **9.** 4.73 m
2. 96 g   **5.** 16 p   **8.** 989 g   **10.** 206 cm²
3. 55.5 cm   **6.** 3.08 kg

11. 2.52 m   **14.** 198 kg   **17.** 0.34 km   **19.** £75
12. 14.4 m²   **15.** 1.44 m   **18.** 1.6 litres   **20.** 198 m
13. 333   **16.** £1.50

21. 90 g   **25.** 320 m²   **29.** 14 p   **33.** 2.1 m
22. 2.94 mm   **26.** 45 km   **30.** £53.43   **34.** £10
23. 18 cm   **27.** 5 km   **31.** 48 p   **35.** 2 kg
24. 9 m²   **28.** 149 cm²   **32.** 6 g   **36.** 14 mm

EXERCISE 4g
(p. 56)
1. 40%   **5.** 30%   **7.** 75%
2. 70%   **6.** 75%   **8.** $66\frac{2}{3}$%
3. 20%   **9.** 65%
4. 20%   **10.** 1960

11. a) $46\frac{2}{3}$%   b) $53\frac{1}{3}$%   **15.** 5760
12. a) 52   b) 28   **16.** 78
13. a) 12   b) 18   **17.** £62.40
14. a) 36   b) 204   **18.** 112

EXERCISE 4h
(p. 57)
1. a) $\frac{2}{5}$ b) $\frac{27}{50}$ c) $\frac{11}{40}$ **4.** $12\frac{1}{2}$%
2. a) 60%   b) 78%   c) $12\frac{1}{2}$%   **5.** 54 m
3. 8%   **6.** 97%

EXERCISE 4i
(p. 58)
A vulgar fraction is referred to in Number 1. It needs explaining. It is worthwhile also to point out that "decimal fraction" is the full description of what we normally refer to as a decimal.

1. a) $\frac{9}{25}$ b) 0.36
2. a) $62\frac{1}{2}\%$ b) 133% c) 250%
3. $12\frac{1}{2}\%$
4. $289\,\text{m}^2$
5. £840

EXERCISE 4j
(p. 58)

1. a) $12\frac{1}{2}\%$ b) $37\frac{1}{2}\%$ c) 50%
2. a) 28.6% b) 27.9% c) 122%
3. a) $\frac{1}{8}$ b) 0.125
4. 90 p
5. 54

CHAPTER 5 Scale Drawing

Answers given for measurements are calculated and this accuracy is not attainable from drawings, so allow for this when deciding on acceptable accuracy.

EXERCISE 5a
(p. 59)
Most questions have the scale given but Numbers 6 to 10 do not. There is a short note in the exercise about choosing suitable scales, but much more discussion is necessary. It can be profitable to begin this topic by asking the pupils to draw a simple rectangle, 55 m by 30 m say, choosing their own scales, and then compare results.

11. 500 m   12. 2.29 m

EXERCISE 5b
(p. 63)
Link the words elevation and depression to their everyday use and include words from the same root, e.g. elevator, elevate, depress, depressed etc.

1. 23 m   3. 50 m
2. 22 m   4. 38 m

5. 70 m   7. 55 m   9. 9 m   11. 180 m
6. 32 m   8. 58 m   10. 297 m   12. 91 m

EXERCISE 5c
(p. 65)

1. 86 m   2. 77 m   3. 71 m   4. 81 m

5. 339 m   7. 112 m   8. 923 m   9. 528 m
6. 824 m

10. 54 m   12. 8660 m   14. 134 m   16. 280 m
11. 1170 m   13. 433 m   15. 582 m

EXERCISE 5d Explain the meaning of compass points (can be confused with the point of a
(p. 68) pair of compasses).

1.

6.
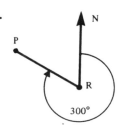

2.
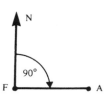

7.
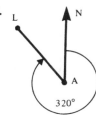

3.
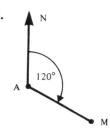

8.
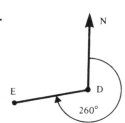

4.
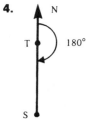

9.
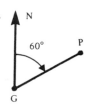

5.
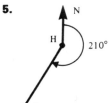

10.
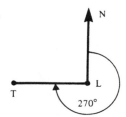

11.

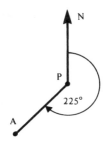

12.

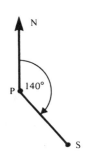

13.

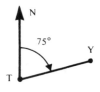

14.

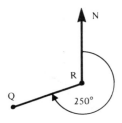

15.

16.

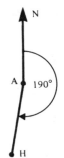

17.

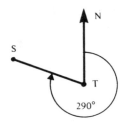

18.

19.

20.

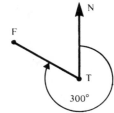

EXERCISE 5e
(p. 70)
1. 87 m   **2.** 163 m   **3.** 274 m   **4.** 51 m   **5.** 1227 m

EXERCISE 5f
(p. 71)
1. 860 cm

2.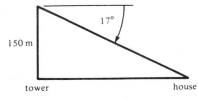

4.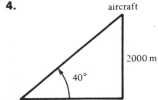

3.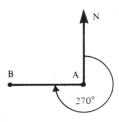

5.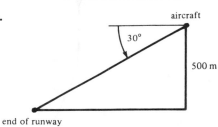

EXERCISE 5g
(p. 72)
1. 94 m   **2.** 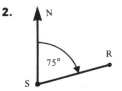   **3.**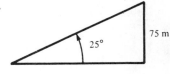

4.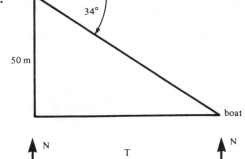

TB̂A = TÂB so △TAB
is isosceles
∴ AT = BT

EXERCISE 5h   **1.** 354 m
(p. 72)

2.
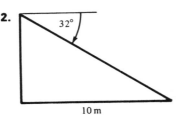

4.
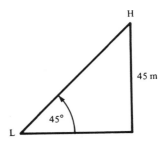

3.
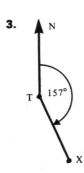

5.
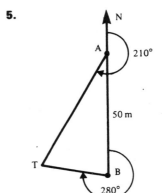

B is nearer to T than A is

CHAPTER 6   Equations and Formulae ━━━━━━━━━━━━━

Much of this chapter repeats work that is in Book 1A, but with shorter exercises.

EXERCISE 6a   Repeats the work on equations in Book 1A. The equations are grouped
(p. 73)   according to complexity and if any of these types are being met for the first
time, supplementary questions will probably be necessary. All will need
reminding about the meaning of $5x$, like terms, unlike terms, etc., and the
order in which it is sensible to rearrange equations.

1. 4	**4.** 2	**7.** 1	**9.** 2
2. 4	**5.** 3	**8.** 3	**10.** 3
3. 12	**6.** 4		

11. 4	**14.** 4	**17.** 3	**19.** −2
12. 5	**15.** 1	**18.** 8	**20.** 1
13. 3	**16.** 1		

21. 2 **24.** 1 **27.** 4 **29.** $4\frac{1}{2}$
22. 4 **25.** 1 **28.** 1 **30.** $1\frac{1}{2}$
23. 2 **26.** 1

31. 2 **34.** 2 **37.** $5\frac{1}{2}$ **39.** 1
32. 1 **35.** 3 **38.** $\frac{4}{5}$ **40.** 2
33. $\frac{2}{3}$ **36.** 2

EXERCISE 6b Repeats the work done on brackets in Book 1A. All will need reminding about
(p. 75) the meaning of a *term* of an expression. If doing this work for the first time
more examples may be necessary.

1. $6x+24$ **4.** $6x-10$ **7.** $6-9x$ **9.** $10x-14$
2. $6x+3$ **5.** $12-8x$ **8.** $35-28x$ **10.** $42+12x$
3. $4x-12$ **6.** $20x+10$

11. $8x+18$ **14.** $8x+4$ **17.** $28x+27$ **19.** $4x+25$
12. $26x+13$ **15.** $21x+5$ **18.** $18x-44$ **20.** $-30x+47$
13. $34x-13$ **16.** $13x+19$

21. $10x+5$ **24.** $-4x+14$ **27.** $-7x+32$ **29.** $21x-19$
22. $-x+12$ **25.** $-10x+14$ **28.** $x+22$ **30.** $-6x+2$
23. $17x-33$ **26.** $36x+26$

31. 2 **35.** $\frac{1}{2}$ **39.** -1 **43.** 3
32. $1\frac{1}{2}$ **36.** 1 **40.** -4 **44.** 1
33. 1 **37.** $1\frac{1}{4}$ **41.** $1\frac{1}{2}$ **45.** 3
34. 2 **38.** 1 **42.** $-\frac{2}{3}$ **46.** $\frac{1}{2}$

EXERCISE 6c Revision of multiplication and division of ordinary number fractions (with
(p. 77) exercises for practice) is advisable before working through this exercise.
Equations of this type occur in the work on ratio and trigonometry.

1. $\frac{x}{2}$ **4.** $\frac{2x}{3}$ **7.** $\frac{3x}{10}$ **9.** $6x$

2. $\frac{x}{6}$ **5.** $\frac{4x}{5}$ **8.** $\frac{3x}{2}$ **10.** $\frac{x^2}{6}$

3. $\frac{3x}{2}$ **6.** $2x$

11. $\frac{5x}{8}$ **14.** $\frac{x}{2}$ **17.** $\frac{2x}{3}$ **19.** $9x$

12. $\frac{x}{18}$ **15.** $\frac{4x}{5}$ **18.** $9x$ **20.** $\frac{2x^2}{3}$

13. $2x$ **16.** $\frac{3x}{10}$

EXERCISE 6d
(p. 78)
Plenty of class discussion is necessary at each stage of this exercise. Numbers 11 to 20 can be done by first multiplying by the LCM of the denominator, as shown for the remainder of the exercise. It is probably advisable to use this method for children other than the most able; the latter can have both methods pointed out.

1. 15
2. 8
3. 48
4. 12
5. $3\frac{5}{9}$
6. $22\frac{1}{2}$
7. 14
8. $8\frac{1}{3}$
9. 8
10. 8

11. $\frac{1}{6}$
12. $\frac{3}{20}$
13. $\frac{3}{2}$
14. $\frac{5}{9}$
15. $1\frac{1}{3}$
16. $1\frac{1}{20}$
17. $\frac{5}{12}$
18. $\frac{7}{10}$
19. $3\frac{3}{5}$
20. $1\frac{13}{42}$

21. $2\frac{1}{4}$
22. $13\frac{3}{4}$
23. $3\frac{6}{13}$
24. $1\frac{11}{17}$
25. $6\frac{3}{4}$
26. $3\frac{1}{2}$
27. $12\frac{2}{3}$
28. 20
29. $-1\frac{1}{4}$
30. $1\frac{5}{7}$

31. $\frac{3}{4}$
32. $1\frac{1}{3}$
33. 11
34. $\frac{1}{14}$
35. $1\frac{6}{7}$
36. $\frac{23}{27}$
37. $\frac{18}{23}$
38. $\frac{1}{2}$
39. $1\frac{1}{7}$
40. $1\frac{2}{3}$
41. $1\frac{1}{6}$
42. $5\frac{5}{6}$
43. $1\frac{1}{22}$
44. $1\frac{18}{23}$
45. $\frac{1}{30}$
46. 7
47. $2\frac{17}{26}$
48. 2
49. $-\frac{1}{4}$
50. $\frac{28}{33}$

EXERCISE 6e
(p. 82)
Use for discussion. Even the most able children are likely to find these difficult.

1. £150
2. 40
3. 30 cm
4. 12
5. 24 cm
6. 5 cm
7. 9
8. 3
9. 12
10. £1000

EXERCISE 6f
(p. 83)
Numbers 1 to 10 revise multiplication of directed numbers. Numbers 11 to 16 use these results for simplifying brackets and solving equations: again a good deal of class discussion is necessary and point out that $-(2x-4)$ can be written as $-1(2x-4)$.

1. -8
2. 15
3. -24
4. -3
5. 12
6. 28
7. 2
8. $\frac{1}{3}$
9. -9
10. -45

11. $-2x+17$
12. $17x-20$
13. $-15x-30$
14. $25-14x$
15. $15x-20$
16. $-9x+6$
17. 2
18. $25x-46$
19. $5x-17$
20. $22x-29$
21. 1
22. 3
23. 2
24. 13
25. $\frac{13}{11}$
26. $\frac{13}{16}$
27. 10
28. 7
29. -4
30. $\frac{7}{16}$

EXERCISE 6g
(p. 85)
These examples on constructing formulae are not very difficult, but a good many examples should be used for class discussion before children are allowed to try any on their own. Note that capital letters and small letters are used for different quantities so a is not the same as A. To some children this is not obvious.

1. $2l + 2w$ **3.** $2l + d$ **5.** $2l + s + d$
2. $3l$ **4.** $5l$ **6.** $W = x + y$

7. $P = 2l + 2b$ **21.** $d = b - a$
8. $T = N + M$
9. $T = N - L$
10. $A = l^2$
11. $N = 10n$
12. $C = nx$
13. $L = l - d$
14. $p = 6l$
15. $A = 2l^2$ **22.** $q = \dfrac{x}{5}$
16. $N = S - T$
17. $W = T + S$ **23.** $L = \dfrac{ny}{100}$
18. $S = N - L - R$
19. $r = p - q,$ **24.** $A = 100\,lb$
   or $r = q - p$
20. $W = Kn$ **25.** $T = t + \dfrac{s}{60}$

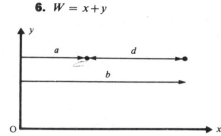

EXERCISE 6h
(p. 87)
This exercise covers an important topic with the future in mind. The importance of putting negative numbers in brackets in the first instance cannot be stressed too much.

1. 10   **4.** 2   **7.** 24   **9.** 25
2. 100   **5.** 20   **8.** 15   **10.** $7\frac{1}{2}$
3. 30   **6.** 200

11. -1 **14.** 33   **17.** 16   **19.** 105
12. -12 **15.** 50   **18.** 2   **20.** $3\frac{1}{3}$
13. 5   **16.** 19

21. 15   **24.** 7   **27.** 0   **29.** 31
22. 200   **25.** $1\frac{3}{4}$ **28.** $\frac{5}{24}$ **30.** -3
23. $3\frac{1}{3}$ **26.** -21

EXERCISE 6i
(p. 90)
1. a) 48   b) -18 c) 6   d) 5
2. a) 4   b) 20   c) 8   d) -12
3. a) 52   b) 20   c) 96   d) -4
4. a) 5   b) 3   c) 38   d) -24
5. a) $1\frac{1}{4}$ b) $4\frac{7}{8}$ c) $12\frac{5}{6}$ d) $\frac{5}{24}$
6. a) 15   b) -1.1 c) -15.9 d) 0.38

7. $C = 50n,$ 600 p or £6   **8.** $L = \dfrac{n}{2},$ £5

9. $V = lbd$, $1200\,\text{cm}^3$
10. $P = 2a + 2b$, $70\,\text{cm}$
11. $P = 6x$, $6\,\text{cm}$
12. $P = L - Nr$, $5\,\text{m}$
13. $P = 3a$, $24\,\text{cm}$
14. $W = Ng + p$, 45
15. $A = 2lw + 2lh + 2hw$, $6200\,\text{cm}^2$

EXERCISE 6j
(p. 93)

Changing the subject of a formula runs throughout the series of books in increasing complexity: this is a first introduction and involves just one operation, except for questions 21 to 24.

1. $T = N - G$

2. $x = \dfrac{z}{y}$

3. $d = St$
4. $X = L + Y$
5. $a = S - 2b$

6. $u = v - t$
7. $d = S + t$
8. $z = P - 2y$

9. $T = \dfrac{C}{R}$

10. $a = L - b - c$

11. $a = P - b$
12. $T = N - R$
13. $c = b - a - d$
14. $u = v - rt$

15. $n = \dfrac{N}{r}$

16. $y = x + z$
17. $c = P - ab$
18. $m = Ln$
19. $u = v - at$
20. $y = s - ax$

21. $r = q - p$
22. $a = s - b - c$

23. $x = \dfrac{z + y}{2}$

24. $L = \dfrac{PR}{10}$

EXERCISE 6k
(p. 94)

1. 6.3, 6.4   (6.32)
2. 9.4, 9.5   (9.49)
3. 5.2, 5.3   (5.29)

4. 14.1, 14.2   (14.14)
5. 8.9, 9.0   (8.94)
6. 11.9, 12.0   (11.92)

7. 6.3, 6.4   (6.32)
8. 14.1, 14.2   (14.14)

9. 4.0, 4.1   (4.08)
10. 17.8, 17.9   (17.89)

11. 2, 3; 2.8, 2.9   (2.83)
12. 3, 4; 3.2, 3.3   (3.27)
13. 3, 4; 3.6, 3.7   (3.65)

14. 2, 3; 2.5, 2.6   (2.54)
15. 3, 4; 3.5, 3.6   (3.56)
16. 3, 4; 3.8, 3.9   (3.89)

17. 2.82, 2.83;   3.27, 3.28;   3.64, 3.65;
2.54, 2.55;   3.56, 3.57;   3.77, 3.78

EXERCISE 6l
(p. 96)

1. $2\frac{1}{2}$
2. $3\frac{1}{3}$
3. $6x - 24$
4. $6x$

5. 12
6. $\frac{1}{3}$
7. $5x - 8$

8. $P = 4l + f + g$
9. -3
10. $N = R + D$

EXERCISE 6m
(p. 97)

1. $\frac{1}{3}$
2. $\frac{2}{3}$
3. $6x$
4. $\dfrac{15x}{2}$

5. $1\frac{1}{2}$
6. $-8x + 10$
7. $5\frac{9}{10}$
8. 15

9. $N = a + b + c$
10. $N = n + ab$
11. b) 3.45

EXERCISE 6n
(p. 98)

1. $\dfrac{15x}{4}$

2. $\frac{1}{3}$

3. 2

4. $\dfrac{11x}{12}$

5. $\dfrac{x}{4}$

6. $x + 6$

7. $-\frac{7}{20}$

8. 10

9. $P = 6a$

10. $P = \dfrac{l}{3q}$

11. b) 3.2, 3.3

    c) 3.2

CHAPTER 7   Coordinates and the Straight Line

It is for the teacher to decide how much, if any, of this work is covered at this stage. It is repeated in Book 3A. However we recommend that Exercises 7a and 7b are covered by everybody: they give an introduction to the idea of an equation of a straight line and provide practice in using coordinates. This section of work is necessary also if transformations are covered from this book (Chapters 8, 9 and 13).

In all cases revision of the use of coordinates is desirable.

EXERCISE 7a
(p. 101)

Everyone can try Numbers 1 to 8. Use the remainder of this exercise for discussion except for the able who can try some on their own.

1. a) 2   b) 3   c) 7   d) 12
2. a) -1 b) -6 c) -8 d) -20
3. a) $-3\frac{1}{2}$ b) $4\frac{1}{2}$ c) -6.1 d) 8.3
4. a) -7 b) 2   c) $-5\frac{1}{2}$ d) 4.2
5. a) 10   b) -8 c) 7   d) -5.2
6. a) -1 b) 3   c) -2 d) $\frac{4}{3}$
7. a) 3   b) -6 c) $\frac{1}{4}$ d) -4.1
8. a) -2 b) 4   c) $-\frac{3}{2}$ d) $\frac{3}{4}$
9. $a = -5,\ b = 3,\ c = -4$
10. $a = -2,\ b = 8,\ c = 18$
11. $y = 3x$
12. $y = -2x$
13. $y = -\frac{1}{3}x$
14. $y = \frac{2}{3}x$
15. $(-2,\ -4),\ (6,\ 12)$
16. $(-2,\ 6),\ (1,\ -3),\ (8,\ -24)$
17. a) above $(2,\ 2),\ (-2,\ 1),\ (-4.2,\ -2)$ b) below $(3,\ 0)$

EXERCISE 7b
(p. 103)

Discuss, with examples, which values of x are sensible to choose and which are not. In the introduction to this exercise we have chosen the extreme values of x: this ensures that the full range of y values is known before the axis is scaled. When the graphs are drawn they can be used to find y values for given x values and vice-versa. Use these graphs to discuss "slope" and "angle made with the x-axis". Point out the need to use a more specific word than slope and so introduce "gradient".

1–6

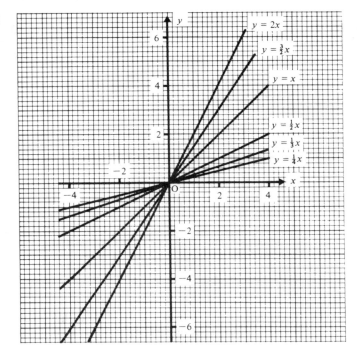

7–12

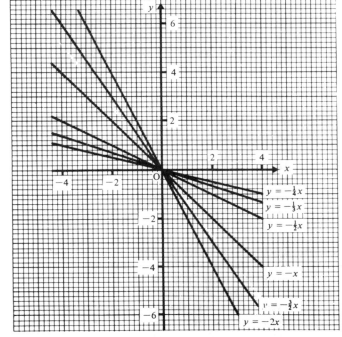

EXERCISE 7c Discuss many examples and include all possible combinations of $\pm y/x$ but
(p. 105) keep away from a decrease in x unless you want to use this to introduce
division by negative numbers. Use the graphs already drawn to discuss
positive and negative gradient and lead to the conclusion that in the equation
$y = mx$, m is the gradient.

This is a good place to introduce division by zero – one of the children may
well ask what happens when the line is vertical. A way to show that division
by zero is impossible is to interpret $12 \div 2$, say, as "how many 2s are there in
12" and to find out by repeatedly subtracting 2 from 12. Then interpret $12 \div 0$
in the same way and conclude that division by zero is impossible (or the
concept of an infinite answer can be introduced).

1. a) 2   b) 2   c) 2   **3.** a) 3   b) 3   c) 3
2. a) -4 b) -4 c) -4 **4.** a) -4 b) -4 c) -4

5. 2.5
6. -0.5
7. a) $+$ b) $-$ c) $+$
      d) $-$ e) $-$ f) $+$

EXERCISE 7d Explain the meaning of steep and steeper in this context. Refer to other uses
(p. 108) of the words, e.g. with reference to hills, rise in price, etc. Emphasise that the
angle between the positive x-axis and a line is always measured anticlockwise.

1. $y = 5x$
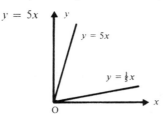

4. $y = -3x$
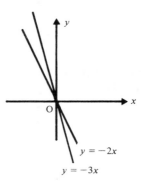

2. $y = 5x$
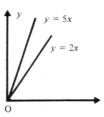

3. $y = \frac{1}{2}x$
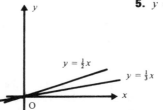

5. $y = 10x$
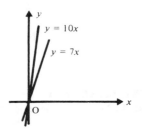

6. $y = -\frac{1}{2}x$

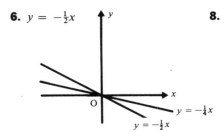

8. $y = 0.75x$

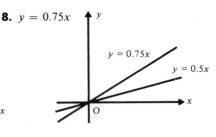

7. $y = -6x$

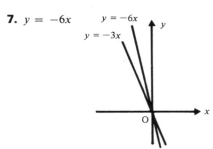

9. acute	**13.** acute	**17.** obtuse
10. obtuse	**14.** acute	**18.** obtuse
11. obtuse	**15.** acute	**19.** obtuse
12. acute	**16.** acute	**20.** obtuse

21. approximately $\frac{1}{3}$, 1, $-\frac{2}{3}$, 0

EXERCISE 7e Introduces *y*-intercept. Frequent reminders of its meaning are necessary.
(p. 110)

1. gradient 3, *y* intercept 1,   a) −5,   b) 7
2. gradient −3, *y* intercept 4,   a) 7,   b) −5
3. gradient $\frac{1}{2}$, *y* intercept 4,   a) 3,   b) 4
4. gradient 1, *y* intercept −3,   a) 7,   b) −2
5. gradient $\frac{3}{4}$, *y* intercept 3,   a) 4,   b) 2

6. gradient 2, *y* intercept −2   **11.** gradient 2, *y* intercept 5
7. gradient −2, *y* intercept 4   **12.** gradient −2, *y* intercept −7
8. gradient 3, *y* intercept −4   **13.** gradient −3, *y* intercept +2
9. gradient $\frac{1}{2}$, *y* intercept 3   **14.** gradient $\frac{1}{3}$, *y* intercept −6
10. gradient $-\frac{3}{2}$, *y* intercept 3   **15.** gradient $\frac{2}{5}$, *y* intercept −5

In Numbers 6 to 15 the value for (a) is the same as the gradient and the value for (b) is the same as the *y* intercept.

EXERCISE 7f Discuss what you expect in the way of a sketch. We feel that pupils should
(p. 112) develop the ability to draw completely freehand sketches, without even using a ruler, but appreciate that labelling the sketch is necessary.

1. $m = 4$, $c = 7$

2. $m = \frac{1}{2}$, $c = -4$

3. $m = 3$, $c = -2$

4. $m = -4$, $c = 5$

5. $m = 7$, $c = 6$

6. $m = \frac{2}{5}$, $c = -3$

7. $m = \frac{3}{4}$, $c = 7$

8. $m = -3$, $c = 4$

9. $m = -\frac{1}{2}$, $c = 6$

10. $m = -7$, $c = -3$

11.

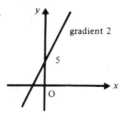

gradient 2

5

12.

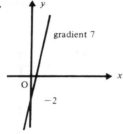

gradient 7

-2

13.

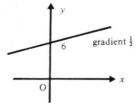

6   gradient $\frac{1}{2}$

14.

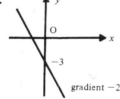

-3

gradient -2

15.

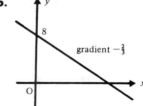

8

gradient $-\frac{2}{3}$

16.

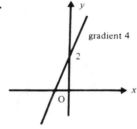

gradient 4

2

17.

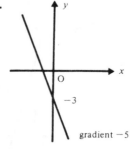

-3

gradient -5

18.

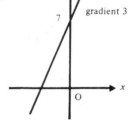

7   gradient 3

19.

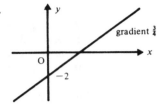

gradient ¾

−2

20.

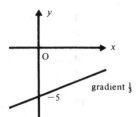

gradient ⅓

−5

21.

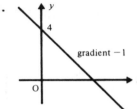

4

gradient −1

25.

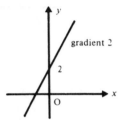

gradient 2

2

22.

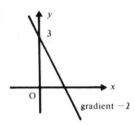

3

gradient −2

26.

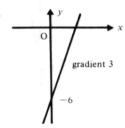

gradient 3

−6

23.

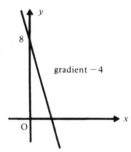

8

gradient −4

27.

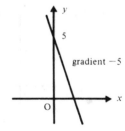

5

gradient −5

24.

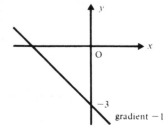

−3

gradient −1

28.

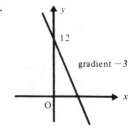

12

gradient −3

29.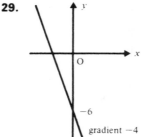

30.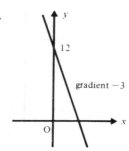

EXERCISE 7g Numbers 11 to 16 require changing the form of the equation.
(p. 115)

1. They are parallel. Their m values are equal.
2. They are parallel. Their m values are equal.

3. Yes	**7.** Yes
4. Yes	**8.** Yes
5. No	**9.** No
6. No	**10.** Yes

11. Yes	**14.** Yes
12. Yes	**15.** No
13. No	**16.** Yes

EXERCISE 7h It can be useful to ask pupils for the equation of a line 6 units to the right of
(p. 116) the y-axis and parallel to it. Similarly for lines parallel to the x-axis. Include
negative values for both.

1.

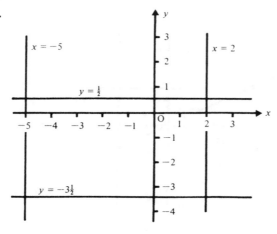

2.

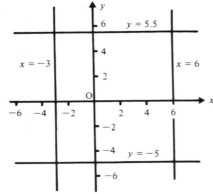

3.

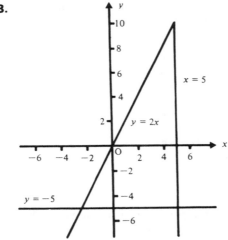

$(5, 10), (5, -5), (-2.5, -5)$
A right-angled triangle

4.

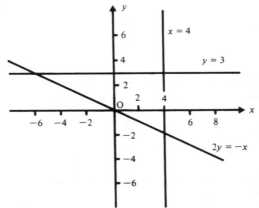

$(4, 3), (4, -2), (-6, 3)$
A right-angled triangle

5.

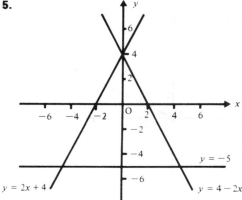

$y = 2x + 4$ $y = -5$ $y = 4 - 2x$ (0, 4), (4.5, −5), (−4.5, −5)
An isosceles triangle

EXERCISE 7i
(p. 117)

1. a) 2   b) −4   c) $\frac{2}{3}$
2. $a = -4$, $b = \frac{1}{3}$, $c = -1.5$
3. a) +   b) −   c) +

4.

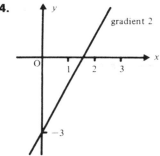

gradient 2

5. a) obtuse   b) acute   c) obtuse   d) obtuse
6. (−1, −6)

EXERCISE 7j
(p. 118)

1. a) 10   b) 15   c) $\frac{5}{2}$
2. $a = -5$, $b = 3$, $c = -4$
3. a) +   b) −   c) −
4. a) gradient 4, y intercept −7
    b) gradient $\frac{5}{2}$, y intercept 1
    c) gradient 3, y intercept 2
    d) gradient $-\frac{1}{3}$, y intercept −4
5. a) Yes   b) No

6.

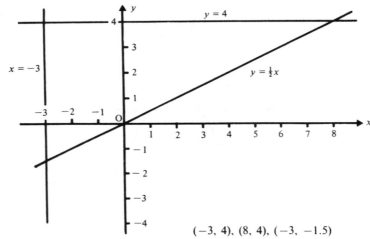

$(-3, 4), (8, 4), (-3, -1.5)$

EXERCISE 7k   **1.** a) 11   b) -10 c) -31
(p. 118)   **2.** $a = -4$, $b = 11$, $c = 5$
                   3.

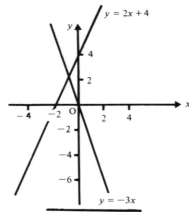

4.

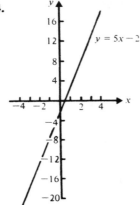

gradient 5
y intercept -2

5. a) $y = 2x - 4$
   b) $2y = x + 10$
   c) $y = -4x - 3$

6.

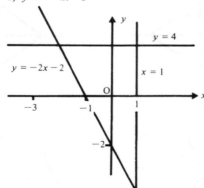

$(1, 4), (1, -4), (-3, 4)$

CHAPTER 8 Reflections and Translations

This topic, together with the work in Chapters 9 and 13, can be done later or not at all. Much discussion is necessary at every stage.

EXERCISE 8a Revises the work on line symmetry in Book 1.
(p. 120)

1. a) and c)

2.   **4.**   **6.**

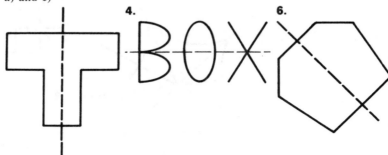

3.   **5.**   **7.**

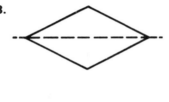

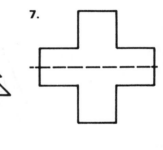

EXERCISE 8b   Revises the work on line symmetry in Book 1.
(p. 121)

1.

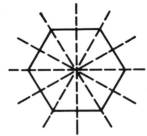

6.

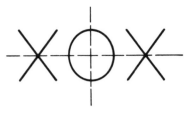

2.

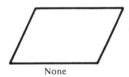

7.

3.

None

8.

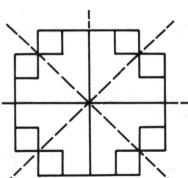

4.

9.

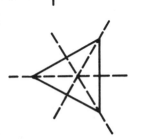

5.

10.

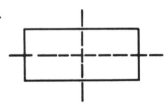

11.

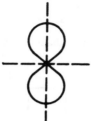

12.

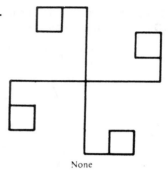

None

13.

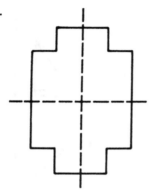

16.

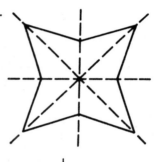

14.

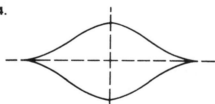

17.

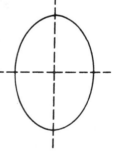

15.

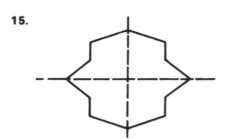

18.

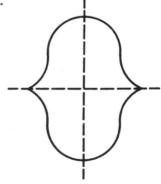

EXERCISE 8c
(p. 123)

The words "object", "image", "mirror line" are introduced. A good deal of discussion is necessary to make their meanings clear.

Numbers 22 to 24 can be done on the same diagram, in which case scale both axes from −5 to 5.

1. 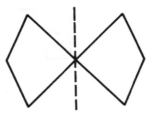   **4.**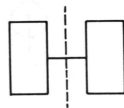

2. 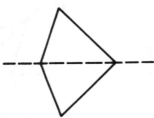   **5.**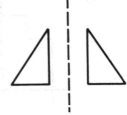

3.    **6.**

7. 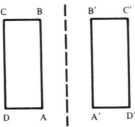   **9.**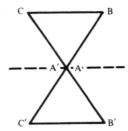

8.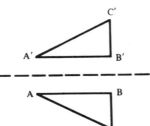

10.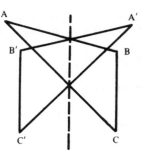

11.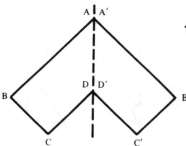

12.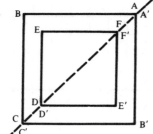

13.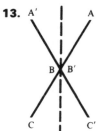

14.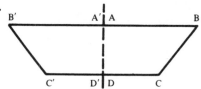

15.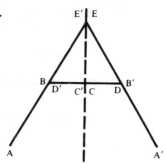

16.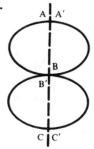

17.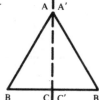

18.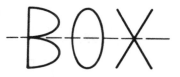

19. Q9: A and A', Q11: B and B', Q12: A, A'; B, B'; C, C', Q13: A, A' and D, D', Q14: A, A' and D, D', Q15: A, A' and C, C', Q16: A, A'; C, C'; D, D'; F, F', Q17: C, C'; E, E'.
They all lie on the axis of symmetry.

20. Equal distances; perpendicular lines.

21. Equal distances; perpendicular lines.

22.

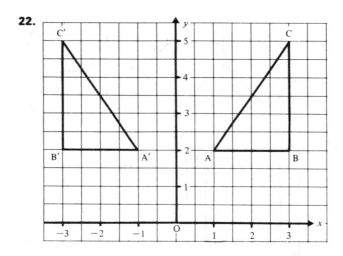

23.

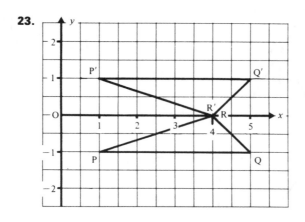

24.

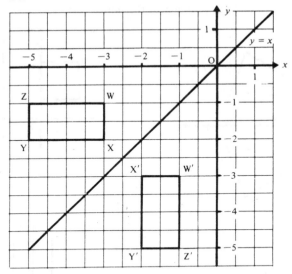

25.

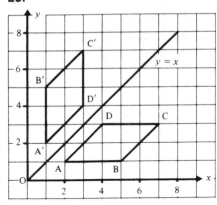

26.

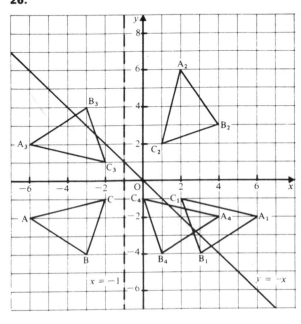

EXERCISE 8d The introduction of invariant points is optional. Able children can be asked
(p. 128)   to find the equation of the mirror line.

1.

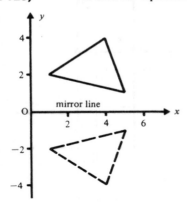

3.

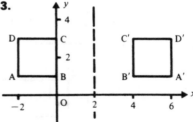

2.

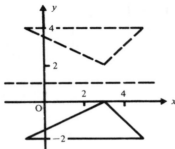

4.

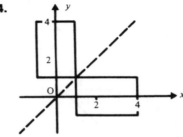

5.

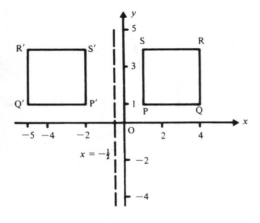

$x = -\frac{1}{2}$

6.

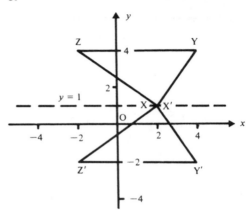

X, X' are invariant points

7.

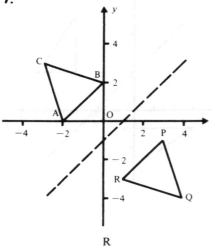

There are none

8.

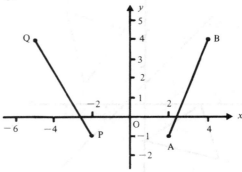

If there is a mirror line it has to be the perpendicular bisector of **AP**. But this line does not pass through the midpoint of **QB**, so **PQ** is not the reflection of **AB**.

9.

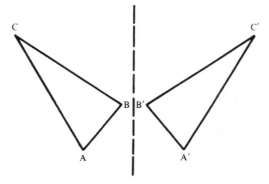

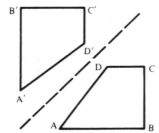

10.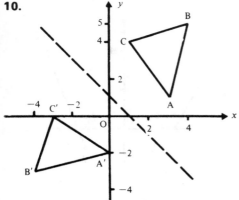

12.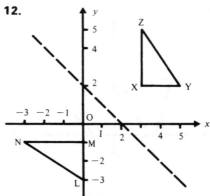

11.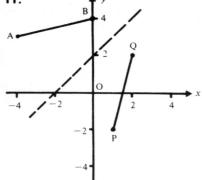

EXERCISE 8e
(p. 131)

1. Yes

2.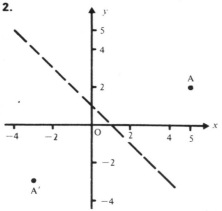

3.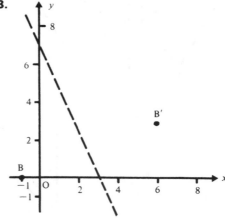

4. Gradient $-\frac{7}{3}$ y intercept 7

Equation $y = -\frac{7}{3}x + 7$ or $3y + 7x - 21 = 0$

EXERCISE 8f
(p. 132)

1. a and c

2. Translation e and b
Reflection a and c
Neither d

3. Translation 2; reflection 1; neither 3 and 4.

EXERCISE 8g
(p. 133)

1.

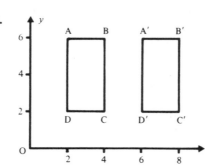

4.

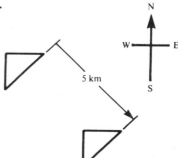

2.

3.

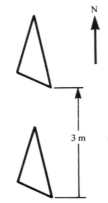

5.

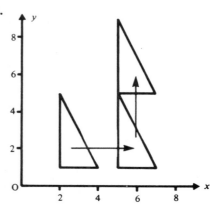

EXERCISE 8h   Revise the work on vectors in Book 1A before doing this exercise.
(p. 134)

1. (7, 3)   **4.** (1, 5)   **7.** (−2, 2)   **9.** (9, −6)

2. (6, 9)   **5.** (1, 3)   **8.** (−4, −2)   **10.** (2, 0)

3. (2, 7)   **6.** (6, −7)

11. $\begin{pmatrix} 4 \\ 1 \end{pmatrix}$ **14.** $\begin{pmatrix} 7 \\ 6 \end{pmatrix}$ **17.** $\begin{pmatrix} -4 \\ -6 \end{pmatrix}$ **19.** $\begin{pmatrix} -2 \\ -2 \end{pmatrix}$

12. $\begin{pmatrix} -1 \\ 1 \end{pmatrix}$ **15.** $\begin{pmatrix} 4 \\ 3 \end{pmatrix}$ **18.** $\begin{pmatrix} -3 \\ 1 \end{pmatrix}$ **20.** $\begin{pmatrix} 1 \\ 1 \end{pmatrix}$

13. $\begin{pmatrix} 4 \\ 2 \end{pmatrix}$ **16.** $\begin{pmatrix} 4 \\ 0 \end{pmatrix}$

21. (5, 6)   **23.** (−2, 3)   **25.** (9, 1)   **26.** (−4, −5)
22. (2, 2)   **24.** (3, 5)

EXERCISE 8i   **1.** $\overrightarrow{AA'} = \begin{pmatrix} -5 \\ 1 \end{pmatrix}$, $\overrightarrow{BB'} = \begin{pmatrix} -5 \\ 1 \end{pmatrix}$, $\overrightarrow{CC'} = \begin{pmatrix} -5 \\ 1 \end{pmatrix}$,   Yes, Yes.
(p. 135)

2. $\overrightarrow{LL'} = \begin{pmatrix} 4 \\ 2 \end{pmatrix}$, $\overrightarrow{MM'} = \begin{pmatrix} 4 \\ 2 \end{pmatrix}$, $\overrightarrow{NN'} = \begin{pmatrix} 4 \\ 3 \end{pmatrix}$, No, No.

3. $\begin{pmatrix} 6 \\ 3 \end{pmatrix}$ **4.** $\begin{pmatrix} -5 \\ 4 \end{pmatrix}, \begin{pmatrix} 5 \\ -4 \end{pmatrix}$

5. a) $\begin{pmatrix} 0 \\ -4 \end{pmatrix}$,   b) $\begin{pmatrix} -6 \\ 0 \end{pmatrix}$,   c) $\begin{pmatrix} 5 \\ 5 \end{pmatrix}$,   d) $\begin{pmatrix} 0 \\ 0 \end{pmatrix}$

6.

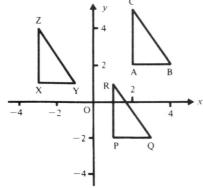

a) $\begin{pmatrix} -1 \\ -4 \end{pmatrix}$ b) $\begin{pmatrix} 1 \\ 4 \end{pmatrix}$ c) $\begin{pmatrix} -4 \\ 3 \end{pmatrix}$ d) $\begin{pmatrix} 0 \\ 0 \end{pmatrix}$

7.

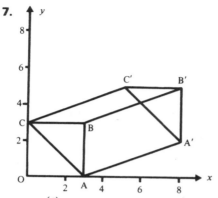

Yes, $\begin{pmatrix} 5 \\ 2 \end{pmatrix}$, parallelogram —the opposite sides are parallel. AA'C'C, BB'C'C

8. a)

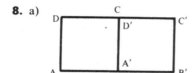

b)

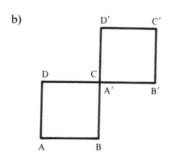

9.

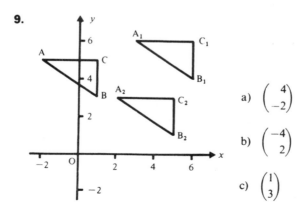

a) $\begin{pmatrix} 4 \\ -2 \end{pmatrix}$

b) $\begin{pmatrix} -4 \\ 2 \end{pmatrix}$

c) $\begin{pmatrix} 1 \\ 3 \end{pmatrix}$

CHAPTER 9   Rotations

Omit if Chapter 8 was not covered. Again much discussion is necessary at every stage of this work.

EXERCISE 9a   Revises the work on rotational symmetry in Book 1A.
(p. 139)
1. a) $\frac{1}{4}$ b) $\frac{1}{2}$ c) $\frac{1}{3}$
2. a), b) and c)

EXERCISE 9b   This extends the work on rotational symmetry a little. It is worth mentioning
(p. 140)   that the order of rotational symmetry cannot be 1 as this would be rotation
through a complete revolution.

1. 4, 2, 3

2. a) 6,   b) 2

3.

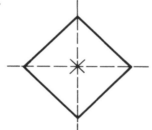

6.

4.

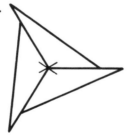

7.

5.

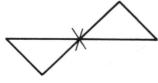

8.

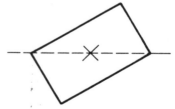

9. 90°, 120°, 180°, 90°, 120°, 180°

EXERCISE 9c
(p. 142) It is worthwhile drawing the diagrams and putting the line(s) of symmetry on them.

1. rotational   **4.** line   **7.** both
2. rotational   **5.** both   **8.** both
3. line   **6.** both   **9.** rotational

EXERCISE 9d
(p. 143) Simple models may help some pupils to see exactly what is going on.

1. 90° clockwise   **3.** 180° either way
2. 90° clockwise   **4.** 90° clockwise

5. origin, 180°   **8.** (1, 0), 180°
6. (1, 0) 90° anticlockwise   **9.** (2, 1) 90° clockwise
7. (1, 0) 180°   **10.** (3, 1), 180°

11.

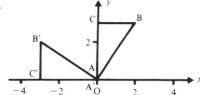

12.

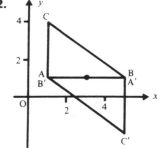

13.

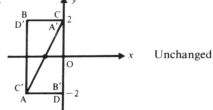

Unchanged

14.

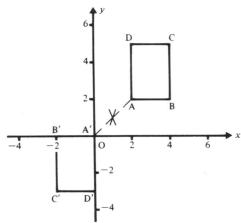

15.

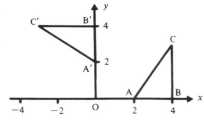

16.

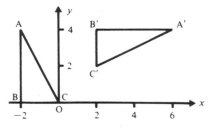

17.

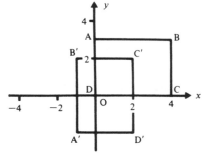

18.

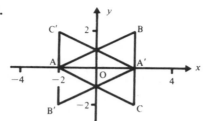

19.

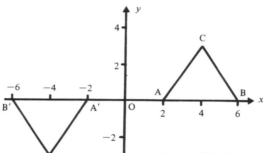

a) a semicircle   b) OC = OC′, OB = OB′

20.

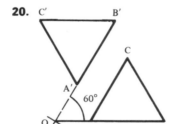

EXERCISE 9e   **1.** c) (0, 4)   e) 90° clockwise
(p. 149)   **2.** c) (−2, −2),   e) 90° clockwise
                 3. c) (−1, 3),   e) 90° anticlockwise

EXERCISE 9f   **1.** 90° anticlockwise   **2.** 90° clockwise
(p. 150)

EXERCISE 9g Simple models may again prove useful.
(p. 151)

           1. Translation given by $\begin{pmatrix} -2 \\ 2 \end{pmatrix}$

           2. Reflection in $x = 0$

3. Reflection in $x = \frac{1}{2}$

4. Translation given by $\begin{pmatrix} -3 \\ 0 \end{pmatrix}$

5. Reflection in $y = -x$

6. Rotation through 90° anticlockwise about $(-1, -1)$

7. Rotation through 90° anticlockwise about $(0, 1)$

8. Rotation through 180° about $(0, 2)$

9. Rotation through 180° about $\left(\frac{5}{2}, \frac{3}{2} \right)$

10. Reflection in $y = x + 1$

11. Reflection in BC, rotation about B through 90° clockwise

12. Reflection in y-axis, rotation about $(0, 1\frac{1}{2})$ through 180°, translation parallel to x-axis

13. 1) Reflection in OB
2) Translation parallel to AB
3) Rotation about B through 120° clockwise
4) Rotation about O through 120° clockwise

14. 1) Reflection in BE
2) Translation parallel to AB
3) Rotation about B through 90° clockwise
4) Rotation about the midpoint of BE, through 180°
5) Rotation about E through 90° anticlockwise

15. Translation given by the vector $\begin{pmatrix} -8 \\ 0 \end{pmatrix}$

16. Translation given by the vector $\begin{pmatrix} 4 \\ 0 \end{pmatrix}$

17.

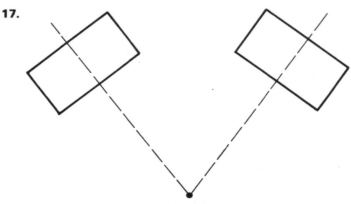

centre of the turning circle

18. Rotations about different vertices, reflections, translations

19.

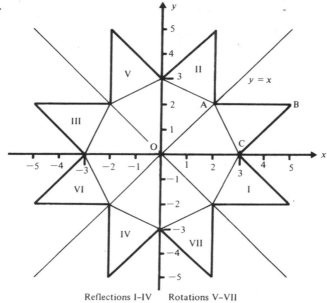

Reflections I–IV   Rotations V–VII

20. a) Reflection in the line $y = -x$ b) Yes

CHAPTER 10 Area

Revise simple multiplication of decimals and fractions.

EXERCISE 10a Revises the work on areas of rectangles in Book 1A.
(p. 157)

1. $43.2 \, \text{m}^2$	**3.** $384 \, \text{cm}^2$	
2. $0.2108 \, \text{cm}^2$	**4.** $40 \, \text{cm}^2$	

5. $3.84 \, \text{cm}^2$	**7.** $0.0008 \, \text{m}^2$	**9.** $1\frac{1}{8} \, \text{m}^2$
6. $24\,840 \, \text{cm}^2$	**8.** $4.56 \, \text{m}^2$	**10.** $4\frac{1}{3} \, \text{cm}^2$

11. $21.6 \, \text{cm}^2$	**13.** $552 \, \text{cm}^2$	**15.** $2870 \, \text{mm}^2$
12. $320 \, \text{cm}^2$	**14.** $672 \, \text{cm}^2$	**16.** $862.232 \, \text{m}^2$

17. $84 \, \text{cm}^2$	**19.** $78 \, \text{cm}^2$
18. $128 \, \text{cm}^2$	**20.** $90 \, \text{cm}^2$

EXERCISE 10b Revises the work on rectangles in Book 1A.
(p. 159)

1. $0.4 \, \text{cm}$	**5.** $5 \, \text{cm}$	**8.** $3 \, \text{m}$
2. $5 \, \text{cm}$	**6.** $1.5 \, \text{m}$	**9.** $7 \, \text{m}$
3. $10 \, \text{m}$	**7.** $1.25 \, \text{cm}$	**10.** $6 \, \text{cm}$
4. $4 \, \text{mm}$		

EXERCISE 10c Counting squares can also be used to illustrate the fact that the area of a
(p. 160) parallelogram is the base multiplied by the height. Emphasise that "height"
means perpendicular height. Use the questions in the exercise to discuss which
dimension is the height.

1. 84 cm²	**3.** 37.2 cm²	**5.** 1280 cm²	**7.** 24.48 cm²
2. 600 cm²	**4.** 0.0288 m²	**6.** 1736 m²	**8.** 7 cm²

9. 38.88 cm²	**10.** 28.8 cm²	**11.** 26.4 cm²	**12.** 352 cm²

13. 63 cm²	**15.** 11.25 cm²	**17.** 36 cm²	**18.** 180 cm²
14. 48 cm²	**16.** 130 cm²		

19. 8 sq. units	**20.** 15 sq. units	**21.** 9 sq. units	**22.** 15 sq. units

EXERCISE 10d Again use the questions to discuss which measurement is the height. A good
(p. 164) example for discussion is that of a tree blown over by the wind:

How high is the top of the tree? How long
is the tree? How high would a helicopter
have to fly to clear it? Etc.

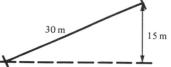

Numbers 25 to 30 are intended for ordinary squared exercise paper. If graph
paper is used, a scale of 1 cm to 1 unit is satisfactory.

1. 48 cm²	**3.** 80 cm²	**5.** 100 cm²	**7.** 24 cm²
2. 1.56 m²	**4.** 3.2 cm²	**6.** 399 cm²	**8.** 14.4 cm²

9. 40 cm²	**10.** 32.4 m²	**11.** 22.2 cm²	**12.** 45 cm²

13. 44 cm²	**16.** 33 cm²	**19.** 24.4 cm²	**22.** 96 cm²
14. 64 cm²	**17.** 75 cm²	**20.** 82.5 cm²	**23.** 21 cm²
15. 540 cm²	**18.** 70 cm²	**21.** 30 cm²	**24.** 8.32 cm²

25. 10 sq. units	**27.** 10 sq. units	**29.** 10 sq. units	**30.** 7½ sq. units
26. 12 sq. units	**28.** 15 sq. units		

EXERCISE 10e
(p. 168)

1. 8 cm	**4.** 2 cm	**7.** 3 cm	**10.** 6 cm
2. 6 cm	**5.** 3 cm	**8.** 2⅔ cm	**11.** 8 cm
3. 6 cm	**6.** 36 cm	**9.** 0.4 cm	**12.** 4 cm

EXERCISE 10f Can be used for discussion with the average but only the above average
(p. 169) should attempt these on their own.

1. 78 cm²	**5.** 60 cm²
2. 22.5 cm²	**6.** 75 cm²
3. 20 cm²	**7.** 18 cm²
4. 54 cm²	**8.** 68 cm²
9. 38.5 cm²	**10.** 48 cm²

11. 24½ sq. units	**13.** 20 sq. units	**15.** 28 sq. units
12. 24 sq. units	**14.** 14 sq. units	**16.** 10 sq. units

EXERCISE 10g
(p. 171)

1. 180 cm²	**3.** 10 cm² or 1000 mm²
2. 20 cm²	**4.** 48 cm²
5. 14 cm	**6.** 6.5 cm

EXERCISE 10h
(p. 172)

1. 6 cm²	**4.** 30 cm²
2. 36 cm²	**5.** 66 cm²
3. 100 cm² or 10 000 mm²	**6.** 6 cm

CHAPTER 11 Circles: Circumference and Area

Calculators should be used freely for all calculations. Revise significant figures.

EXERCISE 11a
(p. 173)

1. 12 cm	**4.** 7 cm
2. 10 m	**5.** 2 km
3. 30 mm	**6.** 9.2 cm
7. approx 3.14	**8.** approx 3.14

EXERCISE 11b We have mentioned that $\frac{22}{7}$ can be used as an approximation to π but with
(p. 175) the use of calculators this no longer seems useful. Those using calculators
with a π button should be encouraged to use it and to ignore the instruction
to take $\pi \simeq 3.142$. If answers are required correct to 3 s.f. then at least 4 s.f.
are required throughout, including the value used for π. If $\frac{22}{7}$ is used, numbers
16 to 23 are suitable: point out that $\frac{22}{7}$ gives π correct to 3 s.f. only, with
corresponding implications for the accuracy of the answer.

1. 14.5 m	**6.** 1570 mm	**11.** 44.0 cm
2. 28.9 cm	**7.** 226 cm	**12.** 176 mm
3. 18.2 cm	**8.** 30.2 m	**13.** 8.80 m
4. 333 mm	**9.** 11.3 m	**14.** 220 mm
5. 54.7 m	**10.** 0.0880 km	**15.** 35.2 cm

16. 970 mm	**20.** 220 cm
17. 88 cm	**21.** 1600 mm
18. 24 m	**22.** 2000 cm
19. 1300 mm	**23.** 29 m

EXERCISE 11c "Quadrant" is introduced in Number 2: quadrant moulding is an everyday
(p. 176) use of this word. For all compound shapes at least 4 s.f. should be used until
the final answer is reached which should then be corrected to 3 s.f.

1. 10.3 cm
2. 10.7 cm
3. 18.3 cm
4. 20.5 cm
5. 27.9 cm

6. 33.6 cm
7. 94.3 cm
8. 62.8 mm
9. 20.6 cm
10. 45.1 cm

EXERCISE 11d Numbers 1 and 2 can be done by everyone. Except for the able, use the
(p. 178) remainder of this exercise for discussion.

1. 78.5 mm
2. 62.8 mm, 88.0 mm
3. 4.40 m
4. 194 cm
5. 176 cm
6. 176 cm, 200
7. 12.6 cm

8. 94.3 cm

9. 62.8 m
10. 6.28 secs, 9.55 revolutions
11. 3140 cm
12. 12.6 m
13. 70.7
14. 94.3 m

EXERCISE 11e
(p. 180)

1. 7.00 cm
2. 19.3 mm
3. 87.5 m
4. 43.8 cm
5. 73.5 mm

6. 132 cm
7. 5.76 mm
8. 62.2 m
9. 92.6 cm
10. 13.9 m

11. 16.5 m
12. 59.8 m
13. 31.8 cm
14. 20.0 m

15. 4.93 cm
16. 9.55 cm each
17. 3.82 cm, 45.8 cm
18. 37.7 cm

19. 4.77 cm
20. 9.55 cm
21. 9.55 cm, 29.1 cm

EXERCISE 11f The demonstration before this exercise is more convincing if the end sector is
(p. 183) cut in half and one half placed at the other end of the "rectangle" as shown
in the diagram on page 183.

1. 50.3 cm²
2. 201 cm²
3. 78.6 m²

4. 78.6 mm²
5. 38.5 cm²
6. 11 300 cm²

7. 45.4 m²
8. 9.62 km²
9. 20 100 m²

10. 25.1 cm²
11. 51.3 m²
12. 58.9 cm²
13. 118 mm²

14. 451 mm²
15. 374 cm²
16. 457 cm²
17. 714 m²
18. 943 cm²
19. 3540 cm²
20. 193 cm²

EXERCISE 11g Numbers 1 to 3 are suitable for everyone but use discretion with the
(p. 185)   remainder of this exercise.

1. 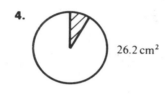 707 cm²

2. 236 cm²

3. 491 mm²

4. 26.2 cm²

5. No
6. 21.5 cm²
7. 8, 110 cm²
8. 11 700 cm²
9. 2

EXERCISE 11h **1.** 17.6 mm   **3.** 37.7 cm   **5.** 491 cm²
(p. 187)   **2.** 9.55 m   **4.** 26.4 m²

6. 28.6 mm   **7.** 7.95 cm²

EXERCISE 11i **1.** 62.8 m   **3.** 57.3 cm   **5.** 89.2 mm
(p. 188)   **2.** 452 cm²   **4.** 50.2 m²   **6.** 40.9 cm

7. 87.5 cm²

EXERCISE 11j **1.** 12.6 km²   **3.** 14 m   **5.** 32.2 cm²
(p. 188)   **2.** 308 mm   **4.** 154 cm²   **6.** 18.1 m²

7. 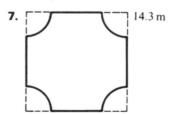 14.3 m

CHAPTER 12   Ratio

EXERCISE 12a Scale drawing can be used as another example: a scale of 1 cm to 500 m can
(p. 189)   be expressed as the ratio 1 : 50 000. Before Number 11, give an example of
comparing three quantities, e.g. using the boat and the two models in the text,
the ratios of the lengths of the smaller model to the larger model to the actual
boat are 1 m : 2 m : 20 m or 1 : 2 : 20.

1. 4 : 5   **4.** 1 : 4   **7.** 16 : 3   **9.** 16 : 17
2. 5 : 4   **5.** 1 : 3   **8.** 1 : 6   **10.** 1 : 1000
3. 2 : 3   **6.** 9 : 200

11. 2 : 3 : 5   **14.** 3 : 4 : 5   **17.** 3 : 4 : 7   **19.** 12 : 1 : 2
12. 3 : 4 : 6   **15.** 5 : 6 : 8   **18.** 1 : 8 : 4   **20.** 14 : 9 : 2
13. 1 : 5 : 10   **16.** 1 : 8 : 7

EXERCISE 12b Revise multiplication of fractions.
(p. 190)

1. 15 : 1   **4.** 3 : 1   **7.** 35 : 24   **9.** 16 : 7
2. 8 : 1   **5.** 4 : 9   **8.** 9 : 4   **10:** 10 : 7
3. 3 : 2   **6.** 7 : 10

11. 8 : 5 : 3   **14.** 2 : 15   **17.** 1 : 2 : 3   **19.** 4 : 3 : 2
12. 2 : 3   **15.** 15 : 19   **18.** 4 : 3   **20.** 3 : 4 : 6
13. 40 : 9   **16.** 5 : 4

EXERCISE 12c Intended for the above average and can be omitted.
(p. 191)

1. 5 : 7   **3.** 5 : 8
2. 13 : 8   **4.** 7 : 10.

5. $6 : 8 = 24 : 32 = \frac{3}{4} : 1$ **7.** $8 : 64 = \frac{1}{16} : \frac{1}{2}$
6. $10 : 24 = \frac{5}{9} : \frac{4}{3}$ **8.** $\frac{2}{3} : 3 = 4 : 18$

EXERCISE 12d   **1.** 3 : 2,   2 : 5
(p. 192)   **2.** 3 : 4,   9 : 16
                      3. 2 : 5,   8 : 3
                      4. 3 : 2,   2 : 3
                      5. 2 : 1
                      6. a) 3 : 2,   b) 9 : 5   c) 18 : 13   d) 1 : 1
                      7. 8 : 12 : 9
                      8. 3 : 7
                      9. a) 12 : 3 : 5   b) 2 : 3   c) 5 : 3

EXERCISE 12e Remind pupils that sometimes $a : b$ is used in the form a/b but that they
(p. 193) should use consistent notation within an equation or sentence, i.e. $x : 4 = 2 : 3$
and $\frac{x}{4} = \frac{2}{3}$ are both correct but $x : 4 = \frac{2}{3}$ is not.

1. 10   **4.** 2   **7.** 6   **9.** 9
2. 4   **5.** 8   **8.** 6   **10.** 12
3. 7   **6.** 12

11. 12, 6, 12

12. $2\frac{2}{5}$ **15.** $6\frac{2}{3}$ **18.** $3\frac{3}{5}$ **21.** $\frac{3}{5}$

13. $1\frac{1}{3}$ **16.** $1\frac{1}{3}$ **19.** $1\frac{2}{7}$ **22.** 10

14. $5\frac{1}{4}$ **17.** $6\frac{2}{3}$ **20.** $7\frac{1}{2}$ **23.** $1\frac{2}{5}$

24. $5\frac{2}{5}$ **27.** $\frac{3}{5}$ **30.** $16\frac{2}{3}$ **32.** $3\frac{3}{4}$

25. $7\frac{1}{2}$ **28.** $3\frac{1}{3}$ **31.** $3\frac{3}{4}$ **33.** $3\frac{3}{5}$

26. $3\frac{3}{4}$ **29.** $7\frac{1}{5}$

EXERCISE 12f Use many more examples for discussion. These questions can be used for
(p. 195) discussion with everyone but only the most able should work on their own.

1. $22\frac{1}{2}$ p   **4.** $10\frac{2}{3}$ cm   **7.** 30 cm

2. 18 cm   **5.** 10.5 cm   **8.** 12 m

3. 98 cm   **6.** 27 cm

EXERCISE 12g Much class discussion, using different examples, is advisable.
(p. 196)

1. 48 p, 32 p   **6.** 16

2. 12 cm, 20 cm   **7.** £2.50, £17.50

3. £20, £25   **8.** a) 252 m² b) 105 m²

4. Dick 15, Tom 25   **9.** 12

5. 30 p, 45 p

10. £8, £10, £8   **12.** 42 m², 14 m², 7 m²

11. 6 cm, 8 cm, 10 cm

EXERCISE 12h Not essential at this stage but an interesting use of ratio.
(p. 198)

1. 1 : 50 000   **4.** 1 : 500 000

2. 1 : 500 000   **5.** 1 : 100 000

3. 1 : 100 000   **6.** 1 : 2 000 000

7. 3 km   **10.** 2 000 000 cm, 10 cm

8. 70 m   **11.** 1.8 cm

9. 200 m

EXERCISE 12i Plenty of discussion is necessary. Ratio is revised and proportion is done more
(p. 199) thoroughly in Book 3A so this exercise can be omitted. Another method for
proportion problems is to multiply by a scale factor: e.g. in the worked
example in this exercise, the scale factor is $\frac{400}{250}$ (comparing page numbers);
∴ thickness of the larger book $= 1.5 \times \frac{400}{250}$ (we want the larger book, so the
larger number goes on top in the scale factor).

1. 12 m   **4.** 3.6 cm

2. 36   **5.** 105

3. 18 cm², 72

6. 2 hours   **11.** 54 minutes

7. 9 hours   **12.** £12 (must buy complete lengths)

8. £11.90   **13.** Hardly any! (no room to work)

9. £8400   **14.** $4\frac{1}{2}$ teaspoons

10. $56\frac{1}{4}$ minutes, $5\frac{1}{3}$ km

EXERCISE 12j **1.** $\frac{4}{9}$ **5.** $8\frac{1}{4}$
(p. 201)   **2.** 5 : 8   **6.** 100 m
                  3. £40 : £52 : £8   **7.** 1 : 1
                  4. a) 2 : 3   b) 8 : 27   **8.** £13.12$\frac{1}{2}$

EXERCISE 12k **1.** 1 : 10   **3.** 2 : 5   **5.** 1 : 500 000   **7.** £12, £6, £8
(p. 202)   **2.** 7 : 6   **4.** 9 : 7   **6.** 5$\frac{1}{4}$ **8.** 510

EXERCISE 12l **1.** 257 : 144   **3.** 10 kg   **5.** 6 : 3 : 1   **7.** 91 : 20
(p. 202)   **2.** 32 : 24   **4.** 33 m   **6.** 3.2 km   **8.** £154

CHAPTER 13 Enlargements

Omit if Chapters 8 and 9 were not covered.

The teacher can introduce this topic by producing an enlargement on the board (e.g. one similar to Question 7 in Exercise 13c). The children need to see the process in action before they do it themselves.

EXERCISE 13a **1.**
(p. 204)

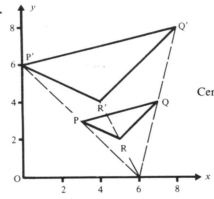

Centre of enlargement is (6, 0)

2.

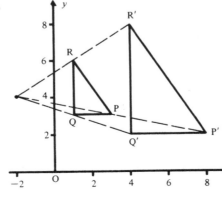

Centre of enlargement is (−2, 4)

3.

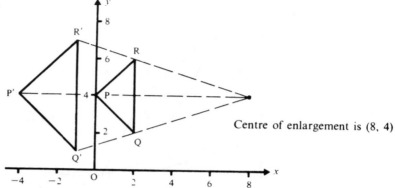

Centre of enlargement is (8, 4)

4. In 1 PQ‖P′Q′, PR‖P′R′, RQ‖R′Q′
In 2 PQ‖P′Q′, PR‖P′R′, RQ‖R′Q′
In 3 PQ‖P′Q′, PR‖P′R′, RQ‖R′Q′

5.

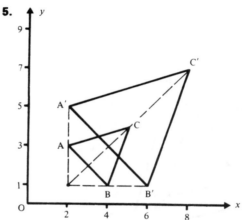

Centre of enlargement is (2, 1)

6.

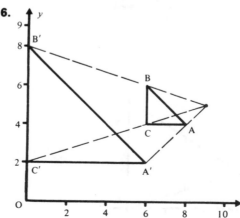

Centre of enlargement is (9, 5)

7.

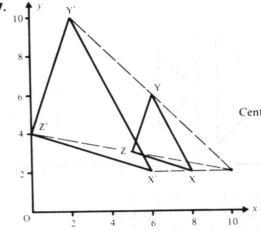

Centre of enlargement is (10, 2)

EXERCISE 13b 1.
(p. 206)

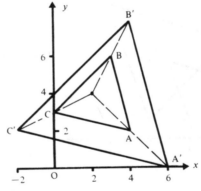

Centre of enlargement is (2, 4)

2.

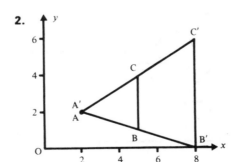

Centre of enlargement is (2, 2)

3.

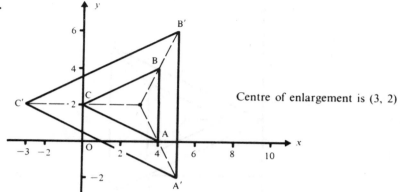

Centre of enlargement is (3, 2)

4.

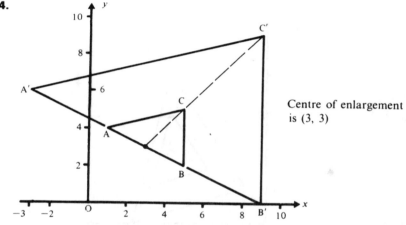

Centre of enlargement is (3, 3)

EXERCISE 13c
(p. 208)   **1.**

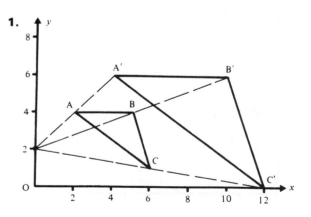

2.

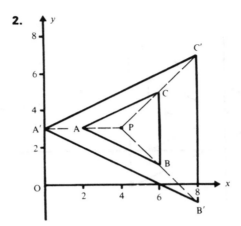

3.

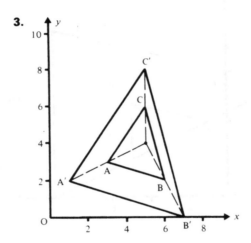

4.

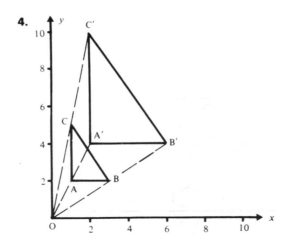

5.

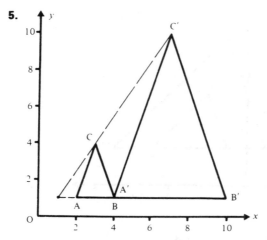

6.

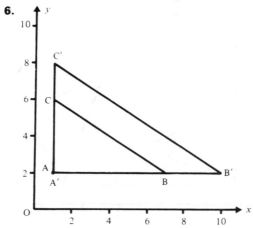

9.

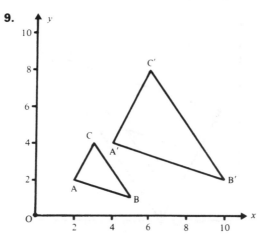

10.

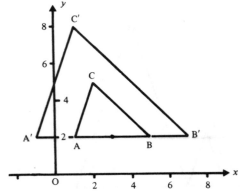

EXERCISE 13d   **1.** (6, 3), $\frac{1}{3}$ **3.** $(3\frac{1}{2}, 4)$, $\frac{1}{3}$
(p. 210)   **2.** (−1, 0), $\frac{1}{2}$ **4.** (1, 2), $\frac{1}{2}$

5.

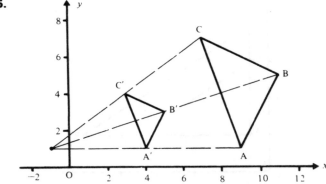

6.

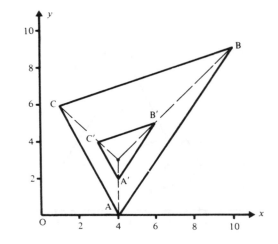

EXERCISE 13e Omit this with all but the most able.
(p. 212)

1. (5, 6), −2   **2.** (0, 1), −3

3.

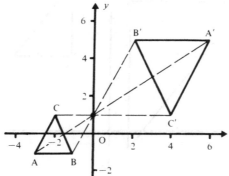

Centre (0, 1), Scale factor −2

4.

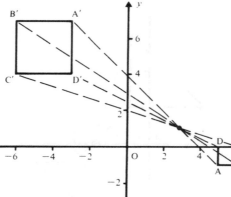

Centre (3, 1), Scale factor −3

5.

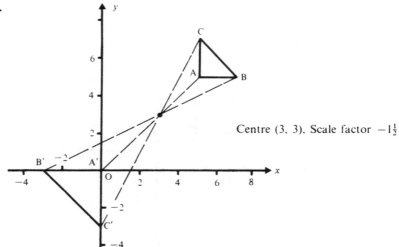

Centre (3, 3), Scale factor −1½

6.

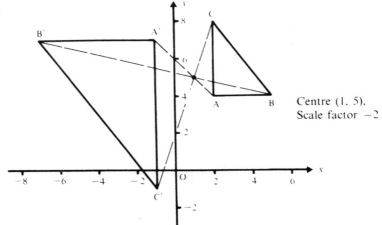

Centre (1, 5),
Scale factor −2

7.

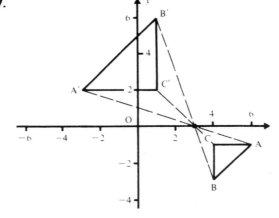

Centre (3, 0),
Scale factor −2

8.

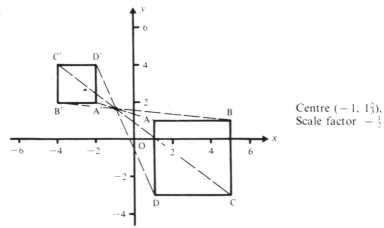

Centre (−1, 1⅔),
Scale factor −½

9.

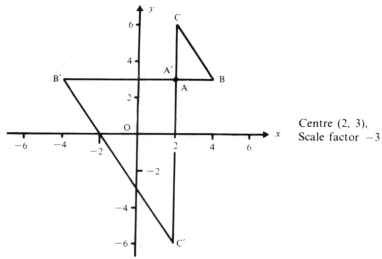

Centre (2, 3),
Scale factor −3

10.

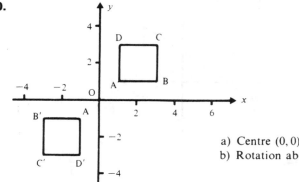

a) Centre (0, 0), Scale factor −1
b) Rotation about 0 through 180°

11.

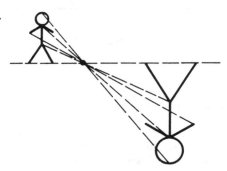

12.

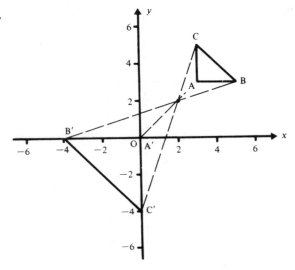

13.

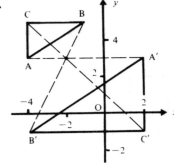

14.

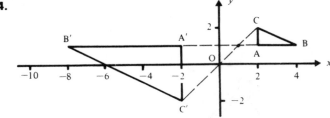

CHAPTER 14 Similar Figures

This topic is covered without much reference to enlargements because we recognise that some teachers may not do any transformation work. If Chapter 13 has been done, then similar triangles can be approached through enlargements and scale factors. For example, in Exercise 14b, you could refer to the object triangle and its image. This approach leads naturally to finding corresponding vertices and appreciating that corresponding sides are in the same ratio.

EXERCISE 14a Give, or extract from the class, further examples before they begin the
(p. 217) exercise.

1. yes
2. no
3. yes
4. no
5. yes
6. yes

7. yes
8. no
9. no
10. no
11. A and D

EXERCISE 14b Number 1 can be repeated when the pupils have had experience of doing it
(p. 218) once. The values for (c) should improve.

1. a) yes   b) AC = 4.1 cm, CB = 3.2 cm, A′C′ = 8.2 cm, C′B′ = 6.4 cm
   c) each is 2   d) all are equal to 2
2. a) yes   b) AC = 8.6 cm, CB = 7.7 cm, A′C′ = 5.7 cm, C′B′ = 5.1 cm
   c) each is 0.67 or $\frac{2}{3}$ d) all equal 0.67
3. a) yes   b) AC = 7.9 cm, CB = 6.4 cm, A′C′ = 3.9 cm, C′B′ = 3.2 cm
   c) each is 0.5 or $\frac{1}{2}$ d) all equal 0.5
4. a) yes   b) AC = 10.1 cm, CB = 6.6 cm, A′C′ = 7.6 cm, C′B′ = 4.9 cm
   c) each is 0.75 or $\frac{3}{4}$ d) all equal 0.75
5. a) yes   b) AC = 6.1 cm, CB = 9.2 cm, A′C′ = 9.2 cm, C′B′ = 13.8 cm
   c) each is 1.5 or $\frac{3}{2}$ d) all equal 1.5

6. 80°, 52°, yes
7. 72°, 72°, yes
8. 70°, 70°, yes
9. 93°, 52°, no

EXERCISE 14c Children need to be shown how to pick out the corresponding sides: either
(p. 221) use the fact that corresponding sides are opposite equal angles, or compare the shortest sides, then the middle length sides, then the largest sides.

1. yes, $\dfrac{AB}{PQ} = \dfrac{BC}{QR} = \dfrac{AC}{PR}$

2. yes, $\dfrac{AB}{PR} = \dfrac{BC}{RQ} = \dfrac{AC}{PQ}$

3. no

4. yes, $\dfrac{AC}{QP} = \dfrac{CB}{PR} = \dfrac{AB}{QR}$

5. yes, $\dfrac{AB}{PQ} = \dfrac{BC}{QR} = \dfrac{AC}{PR}$

6. yes, $\dfrac{AB}{RP} = \dfrac{BC}{PQ} = \dfrac{AC}{RQ}$

7. yes, $\dfrac{AB}{RQ} = \dfrac{BC}{QP} = \dfrac{AC}{RP}$

8. no

EXERCISE 14d **1.** yes, 2.5 cm   **3.** no
(p. 223)   **2.** yes, 7.2 cm   **4.** yes, 6.3 cm

5. 7.5 cm   **7.** $8\frac{1}{3}$ cm
6. 7.5 cm   **8.** $4\frac{1}{2}$ cm

9. 4 cm
10. CD = 9 cm, DE = 10.5 cm
11. 5 cm
12. DE = 18 cm, AE = 13.5 cm, CE = 4.5 cm

EXERCISE 14e **1.** 8 cm   **4.** 30 cm
(p. 227)   **2.** 6 cm   **5.** 24 cm
3. 10 cm   **6.** 6 cm

EXERCISE 14f **1.** yes, $\widehat{P}$ **5.** no
(p. 229)   **2.** yes, $\widehat{Q}$ **6.** yes, $\widehat{P}$
3. no   **7.** yes, $\widehat{B} = \widehat{D}$, $\widehat{C} = \widehat{E}$, they are parallel
4. yes, $\widehat{P}$

EXERCISE 14g **1.** yes, CB = 3.6 cm   **4.** yes, RQ = 7.2 cm   **7.** 5.1 cm
(p. 232)   **2.** no   **5.** yes, AC = $10\frac{2}{3}$ cm   **8.** 3 cm
3. yes, RQ = 35 cm   **6.** no

EXERCISE 14h **1.** yes, 4 cm   **9.** yes, $3\frac{1}{2}$ cm
(p. 235)   **2.** yes, 2.4 cm   **10.** yes, 18 cm
3. yes, 5.12 cm   **11.** AC = 3.15 cm, CE = 1.05 cm
4. yes, 56°   **12.** 143 cm
5. no   **13.** yes
6. no   **14.** 10 m
7. yes, 34°   **15.** 19.2 m
8. yes, 32°   **16.** 60 cm

CHAPTER 15 Percentage Increase and Decrease

Revise earlier work on percentages. Explain the meaning of the words
"percentage increase" and "percentage decrease".

EXERCISE 15a **1.** 150 %   **4.** 160 %   **7.** 148 %   **10.** 112.5 %
(p. 238)   **2.** 125 %   **5.** 175 %   **8.** 400 %   **11.** 157 %
3. 120 %   **6.** 135 %   **9.** 275 %   **12.** 115 %

13. $\frac{130}{100}$ **14.** $\frac{180}{100}$ **15.** $\frac{165}{100}$ **16.** $\frac{230}{100}$

17. 50 %   **20.** 15 %   **23.** 96 %   **26.** $66\frac{2}{3}$ %
18. 75 %   **21.** 65 %   **24.** 34 %   **27.** 47 %
19. 30 %   **22.** 58 %   **25.** $37\frac{1}{2}$ %   **28.** 90 %

29. $\frac{60}{100}$ **30.** $\frac{25}{100}$ **31.** $\frac{66}{100}$ **32.** $\frac{88}{100}$

33. 140   **38.** 849.3
34. 370   **39.** 104
35. 493   **40.** 185
36. 748   **41.** 319
37. 2768   **42.** 2415

43. 70   **48.** 3312
44. 170   **49.** 62
45. 189   **50.** 91
46. 652.5   **51.** 26
47. 2448   **52.** 155

EXERCISE 15b
(p. 240)

1. 63.25 kg
2. £226.80
3. 84
4. 180 cm
5. 33
6. £747.50
7. £8.40
8. £9.20
9. £84
10. £105
11. £750

12. 198 kg
13. 414
14. £110
15. a) £36   b) £76.50
16. 63
17. 94.3 kg
18. a) £5440   b) £4624
19. £1458
20. 27 mpg
21. a) 56 p   b) 616 litres   c) £5.04 less

EXERCISE 15c
(p. 242)

1. a) 16%   b) 0.16
2. a) 45%   b) $\frac{9}{20}$
3. a) 0.85   b) $\frac{17}{20}$
4. 20%
5. 42 m²

6. 125%
7. $\frac{145}{100}$
8. a) 98 cm   b) 960 sheep
9. £43.50

EXERCISE 15d
(p. 243)

1. a) 45%   b) 0.45
2. a) 85%   b) $\frac{17}{20}$
3. a) 0.64   b) $\frac{16}{25}$
4. $42\frac{1}{2}$%
5. 2.17 m

6. 58%
7. 0.82
8. a) 94.5   b) 8.8 miles
9. a) £22.05   b) £147.60

CHAPTER 16 Trigonometry: Tangent of an Angle

The trigonometry section (Chapters 16 and 19) is optional at this stage. It is repeated from the beginning in Book 3A. Discuss the meaning of the word "trigonometry".

EXERCISE 16a In Question 14 we expect angles measured by a protractor to be given to the
(p. 244)   nearest $\frac{1}{2}°$, e.g. $26\frac{1}{2}°$.

(Angles given to nearest half degree)

1. b) $26\frac{1}{2}°$	c) 0.5		**4.** b) $26\frac{1}{2}°$	c) 0.5
2. b) $26\frac{1}{2}°$	c) 0.5		**5.** b) $26\frac{1}{2}°$	c) 0.5
3. b) $26\frac{1}{2}°$	c) 0.5		**6.** yes	

7. b) 37°	c) 0.75		**10.** b) 31°	c) 0.6
8. b) 37°	c) 0.75		**11.** b) 50°	c) 1.2
9. b) 31°	c) 0.6		**12.** b) 50°	c) 1.2

13. $\dfrac{B_1C_1}{AB_1} = \dfrac{B_2C_2}{AB_2} = \dfrac{B_3C_3}{AB_3}$

14.

	Angle A	$\dfrac{BC}{AB}$
1	$26\frac{1}{2}°$	0.5
2	$26\frac{1}{2}°$	0.5
3	$26\frac{1}{2}°$	0.5
4	$26\frac{1}{2}°$	0.5
5	$26\frac{1}{2}°$	0.5
6	37°	0.75
7	37°	0.75
8	31°	0.6
9	31°	0.6
10	50°	1.2
11	50°	1.2

EXERCISE 16b Give a reminder about significant figures. One of the class will probably ask
(p. 247)   about tan 90°. Comment on it and use it as another opportunity to discuss
         division by zero; see the notes for Exercise 7c.

1. 0.364		**9.** 0.384		**17.** 1.28
2. 0.532		**10.** 1.00		**18.** 0.700
3. 3.08		**11.** 1.80		**19.** 0.0875
4. 1.33		**12.** 2.75		**20.** 1.23
5. 1.66		**13.** 0.0699		**21.** 2.61
6. 0.158		**14.** 0.754		**22.** 1.11
7. 0.344		**15.** 0.966		**23.** 3.49
8. 0.213		**16.** 57.3		**24.** 0.306

25.

Angle	Tangent of angle
32°	0.625
27°	0.510
37°	0.754
31°	0.601
50°	1.19

EXERCISE 16c
(p. 248)

1. 0.277	**7.** 0.591	**13.** 0.913	**19.** 0.378
2. 0.568	**8.** 0.285	**14.** 2.94	**20.** 0.0122
3. 0.202	**9.** 0.180	**15.** 1.17	**21.** 2.75
4. 1.74	**10.** 0.0664	**16.** 1.65	**22.** 0.279
5. 2.86	**11.** 1.15	**17.** 2.17	**23.** 0.836
6. 1.05	**12.** 0.642	**18.** 1.98	**24.** 0.969

EXERCISE 16d
(p. 249)

1. 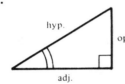   **2.** 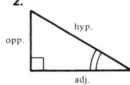   **3.**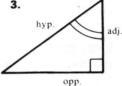

4. 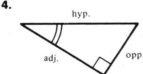   **5.**    **6.**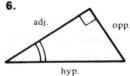

EXERCISE 16e
(p. 250)
In the worked example we chose to form the equation with the ratio of the sides on the left, i.e. $\dfrac{x}{4} = \dfrac{\text{opp}}{\text{adj}} = \tan 32°$. Some teachers, however, may prefer to start with the trig ratio, i.e. $\tan 32° = \dfrac{\text{opp}}{\text{adj}} = \dfrac{x}{4}$.

1. 5.64 cm	**5.** 1.43 cm
2. 5.81 cm	**6.** 5.38 cm
3. 0.975 cm	**7.** 14.1 cm
4. 4.55 cm	**8.** 5.40 cm
9. 7.77 cm	**11.** 7.00 cm
10. 3.12 cm	**12.** 5.40 cm

13. 4.50 cm

14. 7.05 cm

15. 6.43 cm

16. 6.24 cm

17. 16.9 cm

18. 3.44 cm

19. 9.33 cm

20. 10.2 cm

21. 5.22 cm

22. 3.00 m

23. 17.8 cm

24. 9.23 cm

EXERCISE 16f
(p. 253)

1. 5.77 cm

2. 4.60 cm

3. 3.68 cm

4. 5.60 cm

5. 8.96 cm

6. 6.64 cm

7. 9.99 cm

8. 14.1 cm

9. 34.5 cm

10. 3.50 cm

11. 17.9 cm

12. 126 cm

EXERCISE 16g
(p. 255)

1. 14.3 cm

2. 17.9 cm

3. 8.16 cm

4. 10.1 cm

5. 5.10 m

6. 69.9 m

7. 3.23 cm

8. 30.8 cm

9. 5.66 m

10. 1.40 m

11. a) 16°   b) 17.2 m

EXERCISE 16h
(p. 257)
Point out that if the tangent of an acute angle is greater than 1, the angle is greater than 45°. Use the earlier discussion about tan 90° to show that there is no upper limit for the value of the tangent of an angle (but keep it simple).

Answers given correct to 1 decimal place.

1. 65.6°

2. 19.8°

3. 22.3°

4. 76.3°

5. 54.5°

6. 17.2°

7. 9.1°

8. 31.8°

9. 39.0°

10. 34.0°

11. 44.8°

12. 20.6°

13. 29.3°

14. 59.7°

15. 74.4°

16. 64.4°

17. 69.4°

18. 18.4°

19. 25.1°

20. 14.4°

21. 37.6°

22. 40.0°

23. 44.3°

24. 43.6°

25. 20.9°

26. 29.9°

27. 34.9°

28. 39.0°

29. 48.7°

30. 74.4°

31. 51.6°

32. 47.7°

33. 48.1°

34. 59.5°

35. 45.3°

36. 50.4°

EXERCISE 16i Answers given correct to 1 decimal place.
(p. 258)

1. 23.0°	**7.** 64.1°	**13.** 18.4°
2. 34.4°	**8.** 67.4°	**14.** 36.5°
3. 38.3°	**9.** 62.1°	**15.** 48.4°
4. 42.8°	**10.** 17.7°	**16.** 50.7°
5. 31.7°	**11.** 8.4°	**17.** 51.0°
6. 31.2°	**12.** 36.3°	**18.** 45.0°

EXERCISE 16j Answers given correct to 1 decimal place.
(p. 258)

1. 31.0°	**4.** 21.8°	**7.** 51.3°	**10.** 56.3°
2. 38.7°	**5.** 35.0°	**8.** 20.6°	**11.** 6.8°
3. 26.6°	**6.** 8.5°	**9.** 66.0°	**12.** 67.4°
13. 18.4°	**16.** 39.8°	**19.** 23.2°	**22.** 66.8°
14. 8.1°	**17.** 49.4°	**20.** 12.5°	**23.** 24.0°
15. 9.5°	**18.** 59.0°	**21.** 35.5°	**24.** 53.1°

EXERCISE 16k **1.** 42.0°   **2.** 33.7°   **3.** 55.0°
(p. 259)

4. 38.7°	**7.** 22.8°
5. 36.9°	**8.** 26.6°
6. 50.2°	**9.** 59.0°
	10. 8.8°
11. 33.7°	**14.** 36.9°
12. 33.7°	**15.** 33.7°
13. 57.5°	**16.** 24.4°
17. 26.6°	**22.** 51.3°
18. 31.8°	**23.** 38.7°
19. 29.7°	**24.** 47.7°
20. 59.0°	**25.** 30.3°
21. 33.7°	**26.** 51.3°
27. 42.5°	
28. 41.2°	
29. 56.3°	
30. 52.1°	

EXERCISE 16l Discussion is necessary to remind pupils of·the meaning of "bearing", "angle
(p. 262) of elevation" etc.

1. 31.0°	**5.** 10.2 km
2. 26.6°	**6.** 26.6°, 45.0°, 18.4°
3. 59.0°, 59.0°, 62.0°	**7.** 3.08 m
4. 56.3°	

8.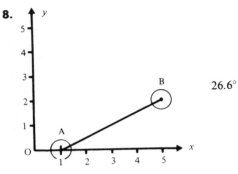

26.6°

9. 75.6°, 104.4°, 75.6°, 104.4°   **11.** 15.4 cm
10. CÂB = 24.6°, 130.8°

CHAPTER 17 Flow charts

EXERCISE 17a **1.**   a) $7 + 5 = 12$ or $5 + 7 = 12$
(p. 265)
b) $12 \div 3 = 4$ or $12 \div 4 = 3$

c) $2 \times 3 - 2 = 4$ or $2 \times 3 - 4 = 2$

d) $3 \times 3 + 4 = 13$ or $4 + 3 \times 3 = 13$

2.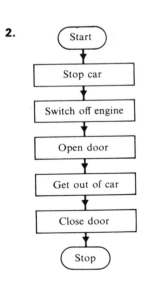

3.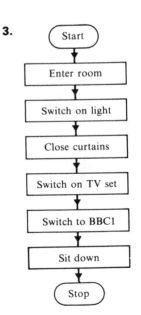

4.

Start

↓

Enter classroom

↓

Sit down

↓

Take out books

↓

Listen to instructions

↓

Start work

↓

Stop

5.

Start

↓

Get cup and saucer

↓

Pour milk

↓

Pour tea

↓

Add sweetener

↓

Stir

↓

Drink tea

↓

Wash up

↓

Put cup and saucer away

↓

Stop

6.

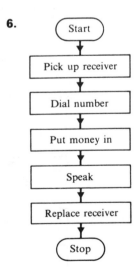

Start

↓

Pick up receiver

↓

Dial number

↓

Put money in

↓

Speak

↓

Replace receiver

↓

Stop

7.

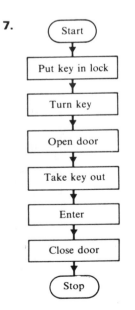

Start

↓

Put key in lock

↓

Turn key

↓

Open door

↓

Take key out

↓

Enter

↓

Close door

↓

Stop

8.   These are suggestions only.

a)

b)
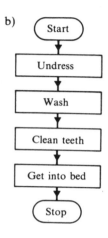

c)
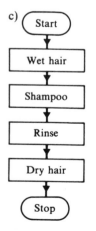

d)
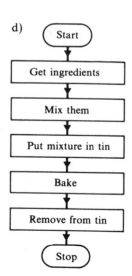

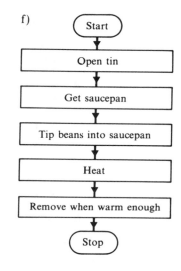

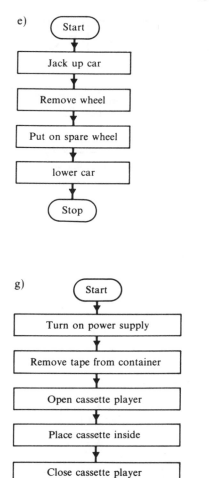

e)

Start → Jack up car → Remove wheel → Put on spare wheel → lower car → Stop

f)

Start → Open tin → Get saucepan → Tip beans into saucepan → Heat → Remove when warm enough → Stop

g)

Start → Turn on power supply → Remove tape from container → Open cassette player → Place cassette inside → Close cassette player → Press correct button → Stop

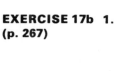 **EXERCISE 17b**
(p. 267)

1.

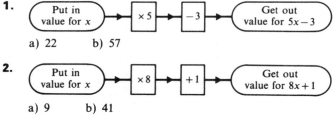

Put in value for x → $\times 5$ → -3 → Get out value for $5x - 3$

a) 22   b) 57

2.

Put in value for x → $\times 8$ → $+1$ → Get out value for $8x + 1$

a) 9   b) 41

3.

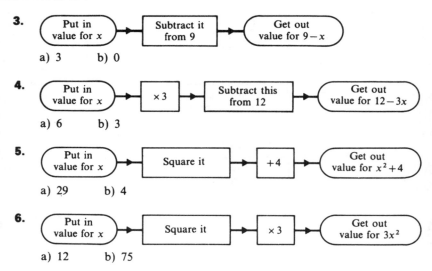

a) 3   b) 0

4.

Put in value for x → $\times 3$ → Subtract this from 12 → Get out value for $12 - 3x$

a) 6   b) 3

5.

Put in value for x → Square it → $+4$ → Get out value for $x^2 + 4$

a) 29   b) 4

6.

Put in value for x → Square it → $\times 3$ → Get out value for $3x^2$

a) 12   b) 75

EXERCISE 17c
(p. 268)

There are alternative arrangements.

1.

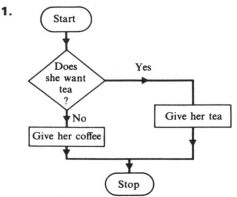

2.

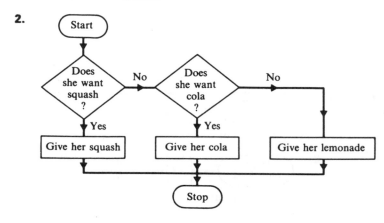

3.

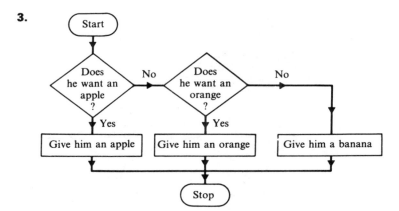

4.

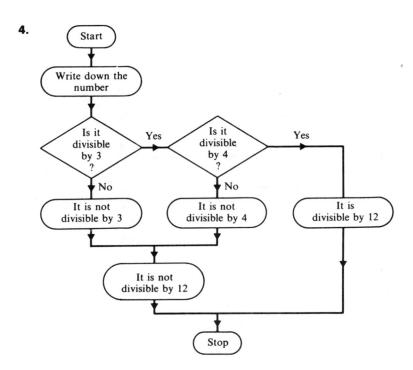

5.

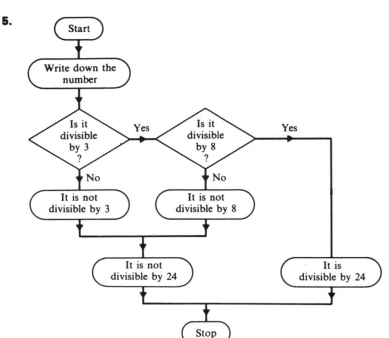

6.

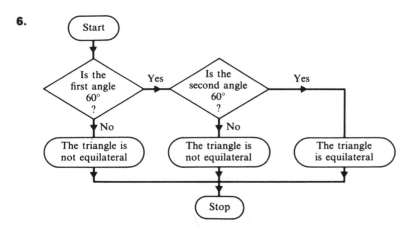

EXERCISE 17d   **1.**   a) To give no more than the first four terms.
(p. 271)   b) 6
                         c)

2. a)

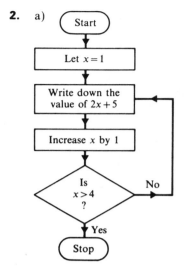

7, 9, 11, 13

b) The same but replace 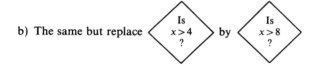 by

3.

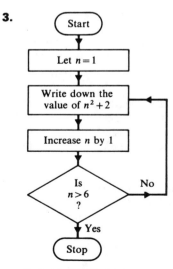

3, 6, 11, 18, 27, 38

4.

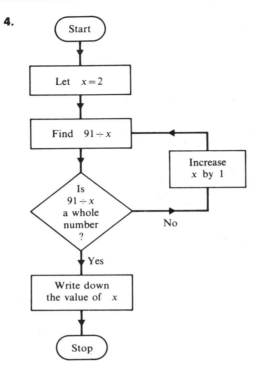

CHAPTER 18 Volumes: Constant Cross-section

EXERCISE 18a Revises the work in Book 1A on volumes of cuboids. Give a reminder of the
(p. 273)   meaning of "units of volume" and why they are cm³, m³ etc.

1. 216 cm³	**2.** 432 m³	**3.** 180 000 cm³	**4.** 105.4 cm³

5. 1600 mm³   **9.** 0.000 008 cm³   **13.** 129.6 cm³
6. 58.5 cm³   **10.** 39 680 cm³   **14.** 133.28 m³
7. 403.2 mm³   **11.** 112.5 cm³   **15.** 144.6 cm³
8. 49.68 m³   **12.** 189 cm³   **16.** 2304 cm³

EXERCISE 18b Discuss actual objects with uniform cross-sections, e.g. a hexagonal pencil, a
(p. 275)   ruler etc. Pupils may need help to "see" that the volume of a triangular prism
is half that of a rectangular one. They need a drawing of the cross-section to
find the area but discourage them from drawing the solid; it is time
consuming, sometimes difficult and does not help.

1. 720 cm³   **3.** 1120 cm³   **5.** 1242 cm³   **7.** 660 cm³
2. 2160 cm³   **4.** 720 cm³   **6.** 128 cm³   **8.** 192 cm³

9. 2400 cm³	**11.** 315 cm³	**13.** 690 cm³	**15.** 864 cm³
10. 2880 cm³	**12.** 450 cm³	**14.** 624 cm³	**16.** 720 cm³

17. 5.184 m³	**18.** 21.6 m³	**19.** 1344 cm³	**20.** 624 m³

EXERCISE 18c Ask for actual objects that are cylinders. An interesting discussion point: why
(p. 279) are cylinders, rather than cuboids, used for canned soup, baked beans etc.?

1. 126 cm³	**6.** 15.1 m³	**11.** 322 cm³	**16.** 2810 cm³
2. 113 cm³	**7.** 37.7 cm³	**12.** 407 cm³	**17.** 941 mm³
3. 314 cm³	**8.** 50.9 cm³	**13.** 330 cm³	**18.** 825 cm³
4. 59.4 cm³	**9.** 4520 cm³	**14.** 652 cm³	**19.** 1.60 m³
5. 3.14 cm³	**10.** 1390 cm³	**15.** 70 800 cm³	**20.** 44.0 cm³

EXERCISE 18d The pupils can be asked to describe what these could be sections of.
(p. 280)

1. 1010 cm³	**3.** 34.5 cm³	**5.** 628 cm³
2. 402 cm³	**4.** 204 cm³	**6.** 2160 cm³

CHAPTER 19 Sine and Cosine of an Angle ▬▬▬▬▬▬▬▬▬

Optional at this stage and omit if Chapter 16 was not covered. This work is
repeated in Book 3A.

Revise the ratios of the sides of similar triangles before starting this work. As
an introduction, part of Exercise 16a can be repeated, asking for the ratio of
the opposite side to the hypotenuse to be calculated.

EXERCISE 19a Some of these can be done orally to demonstrate the use of a calculator.
(p. 281)

1. 0.438	**6.** 0.951	**11.** 56.5°	**16.** 4.0°
2. 0.995	**7.** 0.289	**12.** 24.4°	**17.** 40.3°
3. 0.429	**8.** 0.073	**13.** 39.7°	**18.** 20.9°
4. 0.603	**9.** 0.886	**14.** 44.7°	**19.** 25.3°
5. 0.981	**10.** 0.946	**15.** 69.6°	**20.** 15.1°

EXERCISE 19b
(p. 282)

1. 8.83 cm	**6.** 2.68 cm	**11.** 44.4°	**16.** 33.4°
2. 6.22 cm	**7.** 2.63 cm	**12.** 23.6°	**17.** 22.0°
3. 1.95 cm	**8.** 2.51 cm	**13.** 36.9°	**18.** 30°
4. 1.07 cm	**9.** 9.54 cm	**14.** 51.3°	**19.** 42.2°
5. 6.02 cm	**10.** 4.85 cm	**15.** 23.6°	**20.** 45.6°

21. 2.06 cm
22. 6.64 cm
23. $\hat{A} = 36.9°$, $\hat{C} = 53.1°$
24. 28.2°
25. 3.72 cm

EXERCISE 19c
(p. 285)

1. 0.515	**5.** 0.498
2. 0.669	**6.** 0.391
3. 0.998	**7.** 0.139
4. 0.708	**8.** 0.971

9. 0.954
10. 0.904
11. 0.070
12. 0.985

13. 64.2°	**18.** 19.4°	**23.** 89.3°
14. 24.6°	**19.** 34.9°	**24.** 42.4°
15. 44.4°	**20.** 55.5°	**25.** 51.1°
16. 45.6°	**21.** 76.1°	**26.** 81.8°
17. 75.3°	**22.** 20.3°	**27.** 32.5°

EXERCISE 19d
(p. 286)

1. 8.48 cm	**6.** 7 cm
2. 2.68 cm	**7.** 3.08 cm
3. 5.07 cm	**8.** 3.22 cm
4. 3.75 cm	**9.** 2.78 cm
5. 10.2 cm	**10.** 0.799 cm

11. 53.1°	**14.** 38.9°	**17.** 41.4°	**19.** 66.4°
12. 41.4°	**15.** 32.9°	**18.** 63.3°	**20.** 56.9°
13. 38.7°	**16.** 60.0°		

EXERCISE 19e
(p. 289)
Many children have difficulty in deciding which ratio to use. Discuss several different examples. The following mnemonic for SOHCAHTOA may be useful: Some old hands can always have tickets on application!

1. tan A	**4.** sin P	**7.** tan A	**10.** sin N
2. cos A	**5.** tan X	**8.** sin E	**11.** tan X
3. sin Q	**6.** cos M	**9.** cos P	**12.** cos F

13. 81.9°,   31.0°,   48.6°,   33.1°,   59.0°,   68.0°
2.44 cm,   4.90 cm,   6.43 cm,   0.647 cm,   30.9 cm,   13.9 cm

14. 36.9°	**17.** 61.0°	**20.** 3.06 cm	**23.** 1.09 cm
15. 49.5°	**18.** 41.4°	**21.** 32.7 cm	**24.** 2.37 cm
16. 41.8°	**19.** 32.6°	**22.** 0.282 cm	**25.** 320 cm

EXERCISE 19f
(p. 292)

1. 44.4°, 45.6°	**4.** 7.61 cm	**7.** 12.2 cm	**9.** 13.4 m
2. 4.50 cm	**5.** 35.3 cm	**8.** 15.9 m	**10.** 41.8°
3. 71.9°, 18.1°	**6.** 59°, 166 cm		

11. 45.6°
12. BC = 2.69 cm
13. BC = 1.95 cm, $\widehat{C} = 72°$
14. 66.4°
15. $\widehat{A} = 52.1°$, $\widehat{C} = 37.9°$

16. 5.56 cm
17. 52.8°
18. 55.2°
19. $\widehat{A} = 54°$, $\widehat{C} = 36°$
20. AB = 17.0 cm, BC = 10.6 cm

EXERCISE 19g Can be used for discussion.
(p. 294)

1. 48.6°
2. 5.15 cm
3. 51.3°
4. 53.1°
5. 1.69 m
6. 7.45 cm

7. 48.2°, 83.6°
8. Â = 65.4°, 65.4°, 49.2°
9. 7.18°
10. 9.59°
11. 5.74°
12. 2.87°

EXERCISE 19h Only for able children; intended to give the idea, in an informal way, of the
(p. 297) relationships between the sines and cosines of complementary angles.

1. a) 0.643   b) 0.643; equal
2. a) 0.8   b) 0.8; 90°
3. 0.3

4. 0.8
5. 45°, isosceles, 1

EXERCISE 19i   1. 0.9925
(p. 297)   2. 58.5°

3. 0.8829
4. 30.0°

5. 6.25 cm
6. 53.1°

7. 6.75 cm

EXERCISE 19j   1. 0.906
(p. 298)

5. 12.3 cm

2. 68.6°

6. 30.0°

3. 1.00

7. 7.14 cm

4. 21.4°

CHAPTER 20 Squares and Squares Roots

EXERCISE 20a Do not use calculators.
(p. 299)

1. 9
2. 25
3. 81
4. 900
5. 0.16

6. 2500
7. 90 000
8. 0.0004
9. 250 000
10. 100

11. 0.09
12. 4 000 000
13. 0.000 016
14. 1
15. 0.0009

16. 900
17. 10 000
18. 16
19. 0.09

20. 64
21. 1600
22. 1 000 000
23. 4900

24. 0.0009
25. 8100
26. 0.0064
27. 40 000

EXERCISE 20b With very able children, Number 28 can be expanded and much more made
(p. 300) of it.

1. 60.84
2. 1444
3. 6273
4. 0.1681

5. 0.0256
6. 0.001 024
7. 2323
8. 127.7

9. 2632
10. 96.04
11. 146.4
12. 8.644

13. 1.040
14. 185.0
15. 289
16. 1.232

17. 51.98
18. 134.6
19. 58 080
20. 0.6790

21. 0.7726
22. 0.001 310
23. 5242
24. 14.29

25. 0.0603
26. 0.005 184
27. 201.6
28. 20 160

29. 0.020 16
30. 94.67
31. 193.2
32. 0.005 285

33. c) 4.8, 3.2, 9.6, 7.3

34. c) 30, 70, 164, 185

EXERCISE 20c
(p. 301)

1. 55 696
2. 212 521
3. 27 667 600

4. 17 305 600
5. 1049.76
6. 103 041

7. 628 849
8. 38 937 600
9. 2 044 900

10. 4678.56
11. 152 881
12. 21 996 100

EXERCISE 20d
(p. 302)

1. 5.76 cm^2
2. 92.2 m^2
3. 1050 cm^2

4. 1.12 m^2
5. 296 cm^2
6. 2700 mm^2

7. 0.003 84 m^2
8. 105 000 km^2
9. 0.0961 cm^2

EXERCISE 20e Do not use calculators.
(p. 302)

1. 3
2. 5
3. 2

4. 9
5. 10
6. 6

7. 7
8. 8
9. 1

10. 90
11. 0.9
12. 0.8

13. 70
14. 700
15. 0.2

16. 20
17. 50
18. 100

19. 0.3
20. 0.4

21. 0.02
22. 500

23. 2000
24. 0.004

EXERCISE 20f Do not use calculators.
(p. 303)

1. 4.– – –
2. 3.– – –
3. 6.– – –
4. 6.– – –
5. 1.– – –

6. 3.– – –
7. 9.– – –
8. 4.– – –
9. 2.– – –
10. 0.2– – –

11. 0.4– – –
12. 9.– – –
13. 3.– – –
14. 0.7– – –
15. 2.– – –

EXERCISE 20g Do not use calculators.
(p. 304)

1. 30
2. 200
3. 20
4. 80
5. 20

6. 100
7. 50
8. 200
9. 60
10. 100

11. 600
12. 10
13. 20
14. 200
15. 2000

16. 60
17. 20
18. 20
19. 6

20. 3
21. 1
22. 10
23. 60

24. 6
25. 10
26. 3
27. 200

EXERCISE 20h The more able children may be interested in manual methods for finding
(p. 305) square roots. Here is a brief description of one such method:

To find $\sqrt{20}$, first approximate, i.e. $\sqrt{20} \simeq 4$, then proceed as follows:

$20 \div 4 = 5$ Mean of 4 and 5 is 4.5

$20 \div 4.5 = 4.44$ Mean of 4.5 and 4.44 is 4.47 (working to 3 s.f.)

$20 \div 4.47 = 4.474 \Rightarrow \sqrt{20} = 4.47$ correct to 3 s.f.

1. 6.20	**8.** 2.39	**15.** 101
2. 4.45	**9.** 25.5	**16.** 642
3. 20.7	**10.** 8.06	**17.** 27.0
4. 65.0	**11.** 3.35	**18.** 85.3
5. 5.66	**12.** 7.62	**19.** 7.81
6. 3.13	**13.** 4.90	**20.** 2700
7. 8.19	**14.** 4.36	**21.** 10.7

22. 37.4, 250, 25.0, 84.9, 26.8, 118, 57.1, 204, 64.5, 122, 629, 19.9, 27.5, 275, 2750, 64.2, 27.0, 3.91, 1.92, 6.28, 19.9

EXERCISE 20i
(p. 306)

1. 0.205	**8.** 0.527	**15.** 0.208
2. 0.648	**9.** 0.167	**16.** 0.0980
3. 0.118	**10.** 0.0527	**17.** 0.912
4. 0.748	**11.** 0.548	**18.** 0.566
5. 0.0118	**12.** 0.416	**19.** 0.228
6. 0.707	**13.** 0.447	**20.** 0.866
7. 0.775	**14.** 0.831	**21.** 0.008 54

EXERCISE 20j
(p. 306)

1. 9.22 cm	**5.** 0.245 m	**9.** 0.0922 km
2. 11.0 cm	**6.** 3.89 cm	**10.** 7.68 cm
3. 22.4 m	**7.** 27.4 mm	**11.** 15.5 m
4. 5.66 m	**8.** 290 km	**12.** 7.81 cm

CHAPTER 21   Pythagoras' Theorem

EXERCISE 21a Some historical background would interest most children.
(p. 307)

1. 10 cm	**4.** 13 cm
2. 11.7 cm	**5.** 11.4 cm
3. 9.43 cm	**6.** 13.9 cm

7. The square of the third side is equal to the sum of the squares of the other two.

EXERCISE 21b
(p. 308)

1. 10 cm	**4.** 9.85 cm	**7.** 11.7 cm	**9.** 12.1 cm
2. 13 cm	**5.** 10.8 cm	**8.** 12.6 cm	**10.** 10.4 cm
3. 20 cm	**6.** 10.6 cm		

11. 3.61 cm	**12.** 11.4 cm	**13.** 6.40 m	**14.** 11.4 m	**15.** 12.2 cm

16. 5.40 cm	**18.** 3.31 cm	**20.** 44.7 m
17. 121 cm	**19.** 9.57 cm	**21.** 0.361 cm

22. 8.64 cm	**24.** 2.61 cm	**26.** 13.0 m
23. 17.4 m	**25.** 35.0 cm	**27.** 12.0 cm

EXERCISE 21c
(p. 312)

1. 30 cm	**3.** 130 mm	**5.** 26 m	**7.** $2\frac{1}{2}$ cm
2. 18.4 cm	**4.** 7.5 cm	**6.** 32.0 cm	**8.** 12.8 cm

EXERCISE 21d
(p. 313)

1. 12 cm	**2.** 48 cm	**3.** 24 cm	**4.** 10 m
5. 4.90 cm	**8.** 4.58 cm	**11.** 6.24 cm	**13.** 6.71 cm
6. 2.65 cm	**9.** 7.48 m	**12.** 16 cm	**14.** 13.7 cm
7. 1.73 m	**10.** 7.94 cm		

EXERCISE 21e
(p. 315)

1. 6.71 cm	**4.** 5.66 cm	
2. 8.67 cm	**5.** 11.5 cm	
3. 55 cm	**6.** 9 cm	
7. 3.46 cm	**10.** 265 cm	**13.** 6.8 m
8. 8.15 m	**11.** 9.27 cm	**14.** 89.6 cm
9. 88.5 cm	**12.** 2.5 cm	**15.** 3.51 m

EXERCISE 21f
(p. 317)

1. 12.5 cm	**2.** 10 cm	**3.** 15.0 cm, 30 cm
4. 4.25 cm	**5.** 11.3 cm	

EXERCISE 21g
(p. 319)

1. 2.71 cm	**3.** 10.4 cm	**5.** 12.7 cm
2. 4.69 cm	**4.** 16.2 cm	

EXERCISE 21h
(p. 320)

1. 2.60 m	**6.** 74.3 m
2. 7.81 cm	**7.** 83.1 m
3. 14.1 cm	**8.** 1.63 m
4. 105 m	**9.** 14.1 cm
5. 7.55 m	**10.** 6.22 km

EXERCISE 21i Omit if trigonometry has not been taught.
(p. 322)

1. 71.14 cm; 45.6°, 45.6°, 88.8°	**6.** a) 27.2 km b) 54°, 306°, 126°
2. 2.65 m, 41.4°	**7.** 17.9 cm, 20 cm
3. 18.9 km, 058°	**8.** 7.81
4. 16.4 cm, 66.6°, 113.4°	**9.** 7.07
5. 10.6 m, 22.6 m	**10.** 12.6

CHAPTER 22 Practical Applications of Graphs

Plenty of discussion using different examples is necessary on choice of sensible scales and on which quantity to put on which axis: the horizontal axis should be used for the quantity which changes steadily (time, age, . . .) or the quantity that we start with (e.g. £ if converting £ to $).

EXERCISE 22a The answers given are probably more accurate than those found from most
(p. 325)   pupils' graphs. This could be used to emphasise the need for sharp pencils,
         etc.

   1. a) 36°C   b) 78°C   c) 77°F   d) 176°F
   2. a) £112   b) £67   c) $174   d) $109
   3. a) 496 F   b) 1023 F   c) 142 DM   d) 316 DM
   4. constant speed   a) 12 km   b) 21 km   c) 1 hour 40 minutes
       d) 3½ hours
   5. constant speed   a) 825 km   b) 2475 km   c) 1 hour 49 minutes
       d) 4 hours 33 minutes
   6. a) 54%, 77%   b) 32½, 52
   7. a) £43.75   b) £84   c) £117.25   d) £114.30   e) £251.43
   8. a) 34 mpg   b) 22 km/ℓ c) 64 mpg   d) 8 km/ℓ (to nearest unit)
   9. a) 39 m/s   b) 166 km/h   c) 65 km/h   d) 49 m/s (to nearest unit)
   10. 9.5 cm, 5.8 cm, 6.5 cm, 9.2 cm

EXERCISE 22b   **1.** a) 1290 g   b) 7 mm
(p. 329)   **2.** a) i) 8¾ s   ii) 15½ s   b) i) 134 km/h   ii) 191 km/h
     3. a) i) 305 g   ii) 930 g   b) i) 65 days   ii) 150 days   c) 240 g   d) 20 g
     4. a) 84 m/s when $t = 4.55$ b) i) 81 m/s   ii) 61.5 m/s
       c) 2.25 s and 6.6 s
     5. a) 19 knots, £16.40   b) 14.5 knots and 24.2 knots   c) i) £17.57
       ii) £17.04
     6. a) i) 386 g   ii) 1340 g   b) i) 3.82 cm   ii) 5.5 cm
     7. a) 9.2°C, 7.4°C   b) 11 25 am, 9.30 pm
     8. a) 1612   b) 13 November
     9. a) 2108   b) 14 August
     10. a) i) 1.7 cm   ii) 10 cm   b) i) 1.3 cm   ii) 8.6 cm

CHAPTER 23 Averages ▬▬▬▬▬▬▬▬▬▬▬▬▬▬▬▬▬▬▬▬▬

Do not progress too quickly; this is a frequently misunderstood topic. Try to
keep close to the pupils' experience.

EXERCISE 23a Use the results of Numbers 11 to 20 to discuss the interpretation of the mean
(p. 334)   in each case.

   1. 8   **4.** 29   **7.** 3   **10.** 3.5
   2. 7   **5.** 16   **8.** 40   **11.** 50
   3. 15   **6.** 28   **9.** 6.2   **12.** 0.62

   13. 63   **16.** 63   **19.** 0.875   **21.** 2 mm
   14. 96   **17.** 74   **20.** 5.8   **22.** 86 kg, 81 kg
   15. 16.5   **18.** 1.35

23. 1837 miles
24. 2583 km
25. 72 mm
26. 131.6 hours

27. 134
28. £1.10
29. 92
30. 9

31. 61, 21
32. 233, 193
33. 106, 238
34. 10.5 hours, $3\frac{1}{2}$ hours

35. 68; reduces it to 67
36. 158 cm; increases it to 159 cm
37. 63 610, 12 722, 8294
38. 136.4 kg

39. 160.6 cm
40. 55.6 kg
41. 26

42. 285 cm
43. 2652

EXERCISE 23b
(p. 340)

1. 12
2. 9
3. 1.8
4. 56

5. 5.9
6. 26.4
7. 1
8. 8

9. 155 cm
10. 31, 3
11. 36, 6

EXERCISE 23c
(p. 342)

1. 5
2. 42
3. 17

4. 16
5. 3.2
6. 12

7. 98
8. 36
9. 1.885

EXERCISE 23d
(p. 342)

1. i) 10   ii) 7;   iii) 0.7   iv) 10   v) 0.3   vi) 0.6
2. a) Sandra   (13 compared with 12 on average)
   b) Karen   (range 5 compared with 12).
3. Mean weight for both batches was 20 g.
   Range for Mr Burton's batch was 13 g and for Mrs Burton's was 5 g.
   Ingredients were the same for each batch: Mr Burton was not so expert at
   dividing the mixture into 20 equal portions.

EXERCISE 23e
(p. 343)

At this point it would be useful to discuss the advantages and disadvantages of each
type of average. For example: If five people are employed by a small firm and their
weekly earnings are £400, £90, £80, £80, £60 what is the best form of average to use
for these figures and why?

1. a) 23
2. a) 71
3. a) 45
4. a) 43
5. a) 28
6. 77, 72, 73
7. a) 157 cm
8. a) 54
9. 83, 84, 83.5
10. a) 0

b) 21
b) 66, 67
b) 43
b) 13
b) 27

b) 157 cm
b) 52

b) 0

c) 21
c) 69
c) 45
c) 32
c) 27

c) 157 cm
c) 52

c) 1.5

d) 16
d) 16
d) 7
d) 80
d) 6

d) 10
d) 54

CHAPTER 24 Travel Graphs

All ability groups find this interesting.

EXERCISE 24a
(p. 345)

1. a) 90 km b) 2 hours c) 45 km
2. a) 146 miles b) 5.2 hours c) 28 miles
3. a) 30 km b) 3 hours c) 10 km
4. a) 16 m b) 6 sec c) $2\frac{2}{3}$ m
5. a) 10 m b) 8 sec c) 1.25 m
6. a) 107 km b) 3.2 hours c) 33.4 km
7. a) 150 miles b) 2 hours c) 75 miles
8. a) 50 miles b) 2 hours c) 2 miles
9. a) 20 m b) 5 sec c) 4 m
10. a) 33 m b) 11 sec c) 3 m

EXERCISE 24b The scales in some of these answers have been halved.
(p. 349)

1.

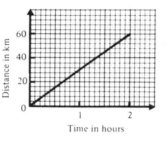

3.

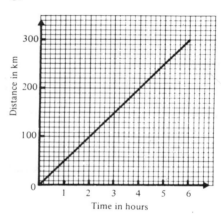

2.

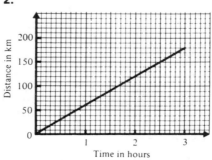

4.

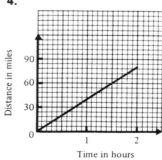

5.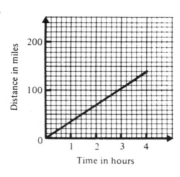

8.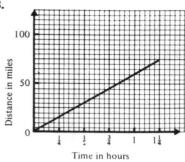

6.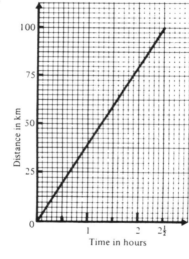

9.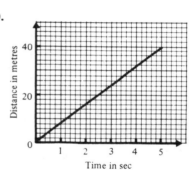

7.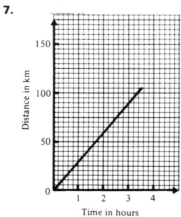

10.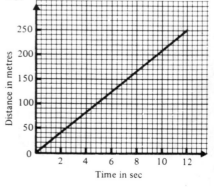

11.

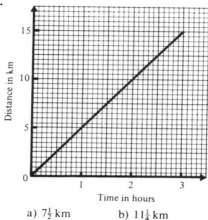

a) $7\frac{1}{2}$ km   b) $11\frac{1}{4}$ km

12.

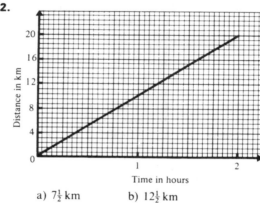

a) $7\frac{1}{2}$ km   b) $12\frac{1}{2}$ km

13.

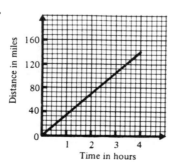

a) 105 miles   b) 44 miles

14.

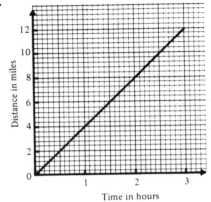

a) 2 miles   b) 14 miles

15. a) 800 km   b) 1100 km
16. a) 48 km   b) 84 km   c) 54 km
17. a) 1200 miles   b) 1650 miles
18. a) 90 km   b) 135 km
19. a) 9 miles   b) 15 miles
20. a) 52.5 m   b) 89.25 m
21. a) 32 miles   b) 38 miles
22. a) 4 km   b) $2\frac{2}{3}$ km   c) 10 km
23. a) 37 miles   b) 185 miles
24. a) 500 m   b) 850 m
25. a) 1755 miles   b) 4185 miles
26. a) 30   b) 72

EXERCISE 24c
(p. 351)

1. a) 2 hours   b) 3 hours
2. a) 5 hours   b) $3\frac{1}{4}$ hours
3. a) $\frac{1}{2}$ hour   b) $1\frac{1}{4}$ hours
4. a) $2\frac{1}{2}$ hours   b) $5\frac{1}{3}$ hours
5. a) $1\frac{1}{2}$ hours   b) 5 hours
6. a) $1\frac{1}{2}$ hours   b) $4\frac{1}{2}$ hours
7. a) 25 sec   b) 200 sec
8. a) 24 min   b) 54 min
9. a) 216 hours = 9 days   b) $5\frac{1}{4}$ days
10. a) $1\frac{1}{4}$ hours   b) $2\frac{3}{4}$ hours
11. a) $2\frac{1}{2}$ hours   b) 5 hours 20 min
12. a) $\frac{3}{4}$ hour   b) $3\frac{1}{4}$ hours

EXERCISE 24d
(p. 352)

1. 80 km/h   **4.** 120 mph   **7.** 50 km/h   **10.** 8 mph
2. 60 km/h   **5.** 20 m/s   **8.** 65 km/h   **11.** 36 m/s
3. 60 mph   **6.** 45 m/s   **9.** 35 mph   **12.** 17 m/s

13. 80 km/h	**17.** 12 km/h	**21.** 54 mph
14. 90 km/h	**18.** 8 km/h	**22.** 54 mph
15. 64 km/h	**19.** 18 km/h	**23.** 60 mph
16. 120 km/h	**20.** 5 m/s or 18 km/h	**24.** 105 mph

25. $51\frac{2}{3}$ km/h	**27.** 80 km/h	**29.** 80 km/h	**31.** 50 km/h
26. 43 km/h	**28.** $42\frac{2}{3}$ km/h	**30.** 90 km/h	

EXERCISE 24e Intended for the above average only but can be used for discussion with
(p. 356) everyone.

1. 9 km/h	**3.** 7 mph	**5.** 75 km/h	**7.** 3 knots
2. 10 mph	**4.** 7 mph	**6.** $125\frac{1}{2}$ km/h	

EXERCISE 24f Use Numbers 7 to 10 for discussion with all but the above average. In
(p. 356) question 10 a ruler can be used to see how the gradients change.

1. a) i) 1215 ii) 1348 iii) 1445 b) $2\frac{1}{2}$ hours c) i) $1\frac{1}{4}$ hours ii) $1\frac{1}{4}$ hours
  d) 64 km/h
2. a) 40 km b) $2\frac{1}{4}$ hours c) $17\frac{7}{9}$ km/h d) $22\frac{2}{9}$ km e) no f) no
3. a) 8 km b) 1030 c) $1\frac{1}{4}$ hours d) 6.4 km/h e) 6.4 km f) yes
4. a) i) 125 miles ii) 175 miles iii) 60 miles b) i) $4\frac{1}{2}$ hours
  ii) 2 hours 12 min c) 80 mph d) 200 miles from A e) noon
5. a) i) 90 km ii) 50 km b) 5 hours c) 28 km/h d) 28 km e) i) 42 km
  ii) 48 km
6. a) i) 1309 ii) 1509 b) 40 miles c) 20 mph d) 30 min e) 13 miles .
  f) 13.54
7. a) 45 km b) $1\frac{1}{2}$ hours c) 30 mph d) 1 hour e) 45 mph f) 32 mph
8. a) 80 m b) 10 sec c) 8 m/s d) 80 m e) 40 sec f) 2 m/s g) $3\frac{1}{5}$ m/s
9. a) i) B ii) B b) i) 80 km/h ii) 64 km/h c) $\frac{1}{2}$ hour d) $2\frac{3}{4}$ hour
  e) 58.2 km/h (counting the stop)
10. a) 8 miles b) 3 c) $\frac{3}{4}$ hour d) $1\frac{3}{4}$ hours e) $2\frac{1}{2}$ hours f) 3.2 mph
  g) the last one h) the first and second

EXERCISE 24g Numbers 3 to 10 are intended for the above average; they can be used for discussion
(p. 368) with the average.

1. a) 150 miles b) 2 hours c) 75 mph d) 1 hour e) 1330; $2\frac{1}{2}$ hours
  f) 60 mph
2. a) 3.06 pm ii) 3.48 pm iii) 4.06 pm iv) 4.36 pm b) 55 miles
  c) i) 50 mph ii) 40 mph d) 18 min e) $36\frac{2}{3}$ mph
3. a) First 34 mph; second 40 mph b) at 11.15, 40 miles from London
  c) 60 miles
4. a) 56 miles b) 45 minutes c) 56 mph d) 36 mph
5. a) i) 0830 ii) 1330 b) 5 h c) $1\frac{1}{2}$ hours d) 4 km/h e) 7 hours
6. a) 80 km/h, 1430 b) 100 km/h, 1354 c) at 1410, 153 miles from A
  d) 52 miles

7. a) Betty, Chris, Audrey   b) 10 km/h   c) 15 km/h   d) 20 km/h
e) at 2.30 pm, after 25 miles   f) Audrey 10 km, Betty 9 km, Chris 15 km
g) $2\frac{1}{2}$ km

8. a) at 3.23 pm, $9\frac{1}{2}$ miles from Jane's home   b) 3.8 miles

9. a) at 3.14 pm, 60 miles from A   b) 6 miles from B
c) 26 miles from A

EXERCISE 24h   **1.** a) 20 km   b) $2\frac{1}{2}$ hours   c) 8 km/h
(p. 375)   **2.** a) 35 km   b) $1\frac{1}{4}$ hours
3. a) 14 hours   b) 57 hours
4. 80 km/h
5. 70 mph
6. 5 km/h
7. a) 15 km   b) $1\frac{1}{2}$ hours   c) 10 min   d) 10 km/h   e) 45 km/h

EXERCISE 24i   **1.** a) 175 km   b) $1\frac{1}{2}$ hours   c) the train stopped   d) 120 km/h
(p. 377)   **2.**

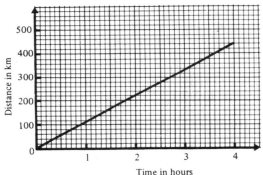

3. a) 900 m   b) 1575 m, 54 km/h
4. a) 3 hours   b) $1\frac{3}{4}$ hours
5. 200 km/h by 5.6 m/s or 20 km/h
6. 12 km/h
7. a) i) 125 km   ii) 260 km   b) $1\frac{1}{2}$ hours   c) $173\frac{1}{3}$ km/h   d) no
8. a) 35 miles   b) Nina, $2\frac{1}{3}$ h; Father, $1\frac{3}{4}$ hours   c) Father, by 5 mph
d) at 1330, 15 miles from Farley
9. 48 mph

CHAPTER 25 Bills and Wages

EXERCISE 25a   Check some actual supermarket bills and go into the meaning of all entries on
(p. 380)   them.

1. £11.32, £8.68
2. £15.36, £4.64
3. £12, £8

4. £15.72, £4.28
5. £15.04, £4.96

6. £
8.40
36.40
4.80
‾‾‾‾
49.60

7. £
1.44
1.56
48
‾‾‾‾
3.48

8. £
4.40
1.68
1.96
‾‾‾‾
8.04

9. £
1.74
1.62
1.80
2.24
‾‾‾‾
7.40

10. £
1.08
42
42
‾‾‾‾
1.92

11. £
63
2.08
96
76
‾‾‾‾
4.43

12. £
3.04
1.50
44
72
‾‾‾‾
5.70

13. £
1.26
1.86
1.68
2.76
‾‾‾‾
7.56

14. £
1.68
3.15
1.53
‾‾‾‾
6.36

15. £
1.75
1.30
54
24
‾‾‾‾
3.83

16. £
37.50
6.50
13.80
15.60
‾‾‾‾
73.40

17. £
51.75
37.60
32.95
4.50
‾‾‾‾
126.80

18. £
7.38
2.79
1.84
4.40
‾‾‾‾
16.41

19. £
3.12
10.35
1.52
57
46
‾‾‾‾
16.02

EXERCISE 25b Discuss gross and net wages and deductions. Discuss also different ways of
(p. 384) calculating pay: are they fair, why are they used?

1. £120 **3.** £93.48 **5.** £148.61 **7.** £220.41
2. £122.50 **4.** £176.28 **6.** £196.24

8. a) 7 hours 40 min   b) 38 hours 20 min, £101.97
9. $43\frac{3}{4}$ hours, £141.75
10. a) $7\frac{3}{4}$ b) $38\frac{3}{4}$, £87.57$\frac{1}{2}$

11. a) £117.80   b) £164.30   c) £173.60   **15.** £171.43
12. £203.94   **16.** £188.37
13. £157.25   **17.** £144.80
14. £201.76   **18.** £176.88

19. a) $7\frac{1}{2}$ hours   b) $37\frac{1}{2}$ hours   c) £106.50   d) $1\frac{1}{2}$ hours   e) £112.89

EXERCISE 25c   **1.** £51.50   **4.** £112.29   **7.** £74.09   **10.** £126.83   **13.** £96.71
(p. 389)   **2.** £68.32   **5.** £104.63   **8.** £150.37   **11.** £70   **14.** £133.84
                    3. £89.30   **6.** £116.21   **9.** £79.75   **12.** £74.81   **15.** £113.06

EXERCISE 25d Be careful with Numbers 13 to 20. Do not suggest that they investigate the
(p. 390) backs of electrical appliances such as cookers, fridges, TV sets, etc., looking
for rating plates. The information is usually in the instruction book and
sometimes in sales literature and discount store lists, etc.

1. 3   **4.** 0.06   **7.** 0.06   **10.** 7
2. $\frac{1}{10}$ **5.** 1.2   **8.** 0.02   **11.** 0.145
3. $1\frac{1}{2}$ **6.** 0.25   **9.** 8   **12.** 2

21. 16   **24.** 3   **27.** 0.144   **29.** 2
22. 1   **25.** 1.8   **28.** 0.56   **30.** 0.84
23. 12   **26.** 1.5

31. 4 hours   **34.** 10 hours   **37.** 3 p   **40.** $1\frac{1}{2}$ p
32. $\frac{1}{2}$ hour   **35.** $2\frac{7}{9}$ hours   **38.** 12 p   **41.** 18 p
33. 250 hours   **36.** $6\frac{2}{3}$ hours   **39.** 3.024 p

EXERCISE 25e   **1.** £35   **6.** £104   **11.** £70.70
(p. 391)   **2.** £42   **7.** £140   **12.** £110.80
                    3. £79   **8.** £48.30   **13.** £93.24
                    4. £100   **9.** £92.78   **14.** £85.44
                    5. £110   **10.** £82.90   **15.** £157.15

16. £135   **19.** £103
17. £98   **20.** £182.20
18. £95.50

CHAPTER 26 Statistics

Throughout this chapter, data extracted from existing databases within the school
can be used to supplement, or even replace, information given in the exercises.

EXERCISE 26a   **1.** a) 3 and 4   b) 6
(p. 394)   **2.** a) 9   b) 5

c) Type of pet	Dog	Cat	Bird	Other pet
Frequency	9	8	5	7

d) 29   e) Rabbit, hamster . . .
f)   It is not possible to answer this.

3. a)

Category	M	W	B	G
Frequency	10	9	6	7

c) 16 males, 16 females   d) 1

4. a)

Number of rooms	1	2	3	4	5	6	7
Frequency	2	2	4	4	7	6	5

c) 5   d) 140

5. a)

Number of blooms	1	2	3	4	5	6	7	8	9
Frequency	0	1	2	3	4	3	3	2	2

c) 14   d) 20

EXERCISE 26b **1.** a) $3\frac{1}{2}-4$ b) No (As soon as data is grouped, some information is lost.)
(p. 396) **2.** a) 59

b)

Mark	30–39	40–49	50–59	60–69	70–79	80–89
Frequency	8	11	18	13	8	12

3. a) 25

b)

No. of words	1–5	6–10	11–15	16–20	21–25	26–29
Frequency	1	3	8	5	5	2

EXERCISE 26c **1.** Whole number   **4.** Continuous
(p. 397) **2.** Continuous   **5.** Continuous
3. Whole number   **6.** Continuous

EXERCISE 26d **1.** a) 8
(p. 399) b) 4
c) $140 \leqslant h < 145$

d)

Height in cm	Frequency
$130 \leqslant h < 135$	8
$135 \leqslant h < 140$	14
$140 \leqslant h < 145$	18
$145 \leqslant h < 150$	12
$150 \leqslant h < 155$	5
Total	57

2. a) 47 kg
b) 5

c)

Weight in kg	Frequency
$40 \leqslant w < 60$	20
$60 \leqslant w < 80$	61
$80 \leqslant w < 100$	13
$100 \leqslant w < 120$	6
Total	100

d) 6   e) 81

3. a) 1   b) 7   c) 20   d) No

EXERCISE 26e
(p. 401)

2.

Weight, w (in kg)	$4 \leqslant w < 8$	$8 \leqslant w < 12$	$12 \leqslant w < 16$
Frequency	7	12	7

5. a) Suggested groups $50 \leqslant w < 55,\ 55 \leqslant w < 60$, etc.

EXERCISE 26f
(p. 402)

1. a) $\frac{1}{4}$ b) $\frac{1}{12}$ c) £45   d) £15   e) £120
2. Bus, 144°; car, 84°; bicycle, 36°; walking, 60°; other, 36°
3. Science, maths 90°; art, music, 60°; English 40°; languages 60°; others 110°
4. Total viewing time 30 hours.
   Comedy series 180°; news 12°; plays and films 60°; documentaries 60°; other 48°

EXERCISE 26g
(p. 405)

1. a)

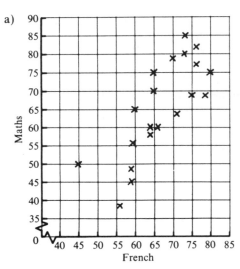

b) Yes

2. a)

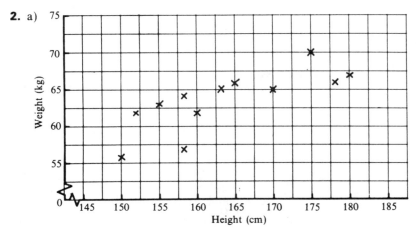

b) Fairly likely

3. a)

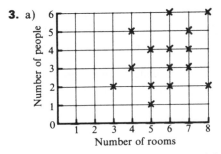

b) Too much scatter to give an opinion.

4. a)

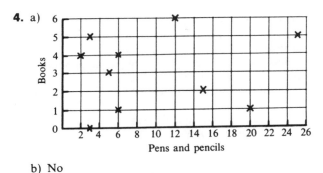

b) No

EXERCISE 26h
(p. 407)
One method of locating this line more accurately is to find the mean values of the two quantities and to use these values as the coordinates of a point on the line.

1. Strong, moderate, weak, none.

Although these exercises can be done individually, the ideas do need thorough discussion afterwards.

EXERCISE 26i
(p. 407)
1. These answers are suggestions only and you may disagree with them.

a) You would normally get enough categories by using whole number sizes only.
b) For half sizes agree to take the next whole number size up.
c) Take the larger size (consistent with (b)). Quite a number of people have one foot larger than the other.
d) Collect the information on paper anonymously.
e) You could get idiotic answers, no answer or multiple answers. It is probably best to collect on paper but with the respondent's name attached.
f) There may be absentees from the class.
   Pupils in another class might refuse to co-operate.

Should boys and girls be considered in separate groups?

2. Method (A) means that there is no way of checking who you have already asked, or of checking someone's reply, or of recording a reply given in an unfamiliar form that will need to be sorted out later.

3. It is worth considering the difficulty in categorizing eye colour.

3. & 4. b) e.g. absentees, embarrassment, height not known, non-co-operation.

EXERCISE 26j
(p. 409)

1. This survey could be carried out in the class. The *aim* of this questionnaire should be discussed beforehand so that the results can be analysed and presented.
Questions (a) and (e) gather straightforward information but notice that the individual answers to (a) and (b) will influence the answers to (c) and (d), so analysis is not easy.
It might be better to compose in class a questionnaire with a simpler outcome if you wish to carry out a survey. It is important for the teacher to be aware of the problems presented by a questionnaire of this type, if only to avoid them.

2. a) Boys and girls grow at different rates at different ages and therefore fall into two separate groups.
b) A numerical scale needs explanation.

3. a) Scale needs an explanation. Words would be clearer.
b) Categories needed.
c) What is meant by 'your family'? Do you include yourself?